ALSO BY MARIANNE MAILI

Lucy, go see.

I am home.
Marianne Maili

Chez Soi Press

Chicago   Los Angeles   Barcelona   Paris

First Hardcover and Ebook Edition published in 2023 by Chez Soi Press
Third Printing, 2
Hardcover ISBN 978-0-9996631-7-2
Ebook ISBN 978-0-9996631-6-5

For all the alchemists and visionaries—
you may be surprised who you are.

I am home.

In Paris, in an April that feels like August, the sun is hot, and women in flowing summer dresses and strappy sandals are sashaying down the sidewalk. Inside the Bar de La Croix Rouge, I sit on a red vinyl banquette. From a black and white photograph on the wall behind me, Paul Newman looks over my shoulder like he could be wondering how to invite himself to my table. I positioned my body for this effect. Windows and doors are open to the street. People around me are sipping their aperitifs, pursing their lips, and barely moving their mouths as they speak. The trees are filling with leaves, now pushed around in the breeze. Memories of my Parisian life are also stirring, generating an electrifying feeling of resurrection.

I have few memories of Paris without clouds. It is a day without clouds. Two weeks of the most beautiful weather I have known in this city.

Paris seems happy I'm back.

La Liberté éclairant le monde–I softly speak, liking how freedom enlightening the world sounds and feels in my mouth in French. I'm reading a plaque on the Statue of Liberty replica, standing on the Île aux Cygnes under the Pont de Grenelle. How free can we be? I wonder as I climb the stairs, then stand on that bridge, thinking about how much freedom costs.

I look to the Right Bank of the Seine and La Maison de La Radio, a round reflective building where a billboard with a larger-than-life photo of me once hung. I see myself decades earlier–a young American woman on a fall day at the end of the 20th century hearing her name called as she slides a letter into a mailbox on the fashionable rue Faubourg St. Honoré. I remember turning toward a nearby café and seeing a woman from California who used to sit next to me in French class at the University of Iowa.

"I knew I would see you here," she says. It's been a decade since we were in class together. She is now a manager of a luxury designer boutique in Beverly Hills and is in town to see the fall fashion shows. She introduces me to the colleague sitting with her, then invites me to accompany them to where they are staying.

We sit on swank burgundy velvet seats and sip champagne at the Hôtel Georges V. When I open my agenda to note my former classmate's telephone number, her colleague looks at it. "You don't seem to have much going on this week," she says.

I pause to consider her intentions, then open a bit while wary. "It's been a great week, hanging out with my man, working on the house and garden, enjoying sunset boat rides on the river," I pause again to sip more champagne and lean back. "We live in a sweet little home with a garden on a river in the Loire Valley where I write and work on different creative projects, and sometimes I come to Paris to audition and work for advertisements, catalogs, and commercials. I love stopping to have fun with friends in different arrondissements at the end of the day. Have you been to the Île Saint Louis? Check out The Regis–it's a great place where I often hang out with friends. From there, I love walking along the Seine to the Gare d'Austerlitz and the train. Once home, we often go to a wonderful water spa. We do stretch classes there, work out, take saunas and steams, and enjoy the different baths. Then it's home for a fire and delicious meal overlooking the river. It's a simple, good life."

"You *definitely* have more time than we do," the woman says.

We all have 24 hours a day, I think, then shrug, guilty as charged.

Next, they invite me to join them to visit the top of the Eiffel Tower.

In the taxi, my former classmate, who once told me I was over-confident, looks at me and asks, "So what kind of jobs do you do in Paris?"

We are stopped at a red light near La Maison de la Radio. I point to the giant billboard with the photo of me on it. "That kind," I say.

I was often ashamed to tell people I worked as a model, embarrassed about making money off my looks. I knew this might make people think of me as stupid and shallow. Yet, I made a month's—sometimes a half or full year's—modest living in a day or less. Finding a way to afford a way of life I love felt smart.

And there were many fun times, like being photographed strutting around Paris, surrounded by spectators, for an ad for a Waterman fountain pen. And another day in Paris, walking with my head hung, feeling far from home and sorry for myself because of it, I looked up to cross the street and three billboards, rotating advertisements like a slot machine, rolled into three photos of me, like a jackpot.

Some people think I'm rich, which I am in many ways, aside from money. I don't own a lot of stuff. I do enjoy time and travel and take spending risks. Sometimes I fall short. It is difficult to accept that financial concerns restrain my freedom, but they do. Anyway, I've invested the money I've made in taking care of myself and living. My life, and even my body, have been my real estate up to this point—a moveable feast like Paris. As far as retirement is concerned, it remains to be seen how I pull that off.

Entering my forties, I asked my agent how much time he thought I had left modeling and acting. "Well, they don't send a letter," he said, "They just stop calling." That's when my love of learning led me to work on a Master's and PhD at the University of Barcelona. I kept modeling and acting, eventually adding teaching, translating, and editing to my work life. I was also a mother of a young boy by that time.

Then came the day when I put my modeling portfolio in storage, choosing to move my concentration more fully from exterior to interior. Sweetly, for my last modeling job before leaving Europe, twenty-seven years after the first, I played a doctor.

L es Oiseaux café on rue de Sevres.

Les oiseaux (Lays-wa-zo) means the birds.

Mom loved birds. I am making this trip with my share of her life insurance. "What are you going to do when the money runs out?" A sister will ask in the near future.

"It won't," I will answer. I will figure things out as I always have. The only time I knew how much money I would make every month was recent, during four years of teaching at American universities. Even then, I was only sure for a semester, then one academic year at a time.

This birdy café in Paris is an old haunt, I often enjoyed myself here alone, with friends, or I'd meet my French lover (the one who became my husband) here sometimes, too. A lighted globe that looks like the one my son's French grandma sent him is perched on top of a glass refrigerator filled with mouth-watering desserts. I notice the young waiter watching, admiring me. I think about a film I saw with Catherine Deneuve, where she quickly partakes of a passerby–a young man–on a park bench because she is feeling so alone and tired of life.

I feel energized and alive.

Missing Mom, who's been dead for a couple of months, is less intense here in Europe, where I am less used to seeing her. When I think of her, I see again the piles of snow surrounding her casket and the word *Praise!* etched into it. *Praise* is the last word I heard her speak, her last command. The soft scent of her lingers.

The desire to travel and to spend some time with my son, here on a semester abroad, drew me back to Paris. I stopped in Iceland to see a friend and will stop there again on the way home. My son and I will visit Sitges, our former home in Catalonia, Spain. This trip is a reunion with all that sometimes felt lost after I left Europe behind six years earlier to be near Mom at the end of her life.

As I cross the Seine, I see my long, meandering journey from the Iowa pasture to Paris, from the Mississippi to the Seine to the Mediterranean. The going back and forth, again and again, to these places I call home.

The work as a model was inspired by travel. Making the world my home was the aim. All the love stories of my life–with the elements, senses, kin, learning, movement, people, and more–fueled this adventure.

April 2022. Sunlit baths in France's Montaigne Noire. The scent of lilacs. Clouds floating above the worn pyramid-like hills. A river rushing below. Birds chattering. Across the ravine, spring splays the hillsides in ten shades of green.

Ten pages fanned out on the desk. It seems ridiculous to write about what I don't want to write about. An editor has told me I need to include a summary of my longest romantic relationship in this story. I will eventually disagree. Instead of writing, I walk on mountain crests for hours. I watch a falcon fly.

Gentle and free, these words rise, later, in the bathtub.

Way back when I was writing the first draft, I felt like Gretel, walking through the forest, leaving story crumbs behind to find my way home. And now, here I am.

A Russian refugee/fashion stylist/embroiderer sheltering at the residency comments on the beauty of the scent trail I leave. "It's *Libre*," I say, "I wear it with *Reverence*. There are two."

I hear again a friend in Sitges saying, "You are free, and that is hard. Freedom is hard."

I'm still thinking about the hardness—isn't not being free hard, too?

While hiking to a waterfall, a German artist resident tells me about German women locked in towers for decades for displeasing men or because men wanted their property.

Why do couples boast about how long they've stayed together, tout it as an accomplishment?

Leaving is also an accomplishment, believe you me.

We know, don't you think? We know what won't work out, and we make deals with ourselves, giving up, turning away, or hoping for better with time on some things to have others.

After my son and I see French family in Paris we have not seen in many years, he asks, "Mom, why did you cry when you saw them? I saw tears in your eyes."

I slow my pace, wondering what to say. "My life is a bit of a broken thing right now, babe," I say, "and I guess they reminded me of both the brokenness and the tenderness."

He moves in front of me to put his face in mine. "But they still *love* you, Mom," he says. "That is not broken."

I smile with closed eyes, then look down and away as we walk on, past the tulips in bloom and through the scent of hyacinths in the air. "I wish I could record smells," I say.

I have yet to find a word for how withdrawing love and presence from someone I loved deeply for decades is wrenching even when necessary, how that move affected so many others, and how all that just broke my heart. I could have said it was my heart that was the broken thing, but it was also my life. My life. My heart. Where's the difference?

I cloistered my heart to spare it and put my head in charge. Which, of course, means I cloistered my life. Freedom can be costly.

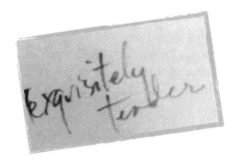

Flakes of snow swirl in the sky as I wake in Reykjavik at a friend's home. It is the First of May, a holiday in Iceland. 2018. We have a spa day ahead. Over a bountiful breakfast of dark bread, cheeses, jams, chocolate, and coffee, we talk about literature, philosophy, and men. "The gifts, courtship, compliments—it seems men are usually setting traps with these," I say.

My friend pours coffee. "Only about five percent of men do not," she pauses, then adds, "An ally is what I want."

"Ally," I repeat. "I like the unified, interconnected sound of that. And the /s/."

S trong and handsome Icelander men massage us. Then we relax–alternating swims in a warm pool, lit blue, with soaks in the hot tub, a sauna, and a steam room.

Warm in white terry robes, we drink champagne and eat chocolate-covered cherries in front of a fireplace with flames shooting out of pebbles. This friend reaches into her bag, then hands me a copy of the first novel I wrote, published three months earlier. I was working on it when we met in England. She smiles and asks, "Could I please have an autograph?"

At her choir's rehearsal that night, I watch and listen to fifty men and women, Icelanders, sing.

"It's what we do here," she says. "We sing. And we sew."

Tiny beads of snow are dropping like pellets when we step outside for a moment.

Back inside, I write as they sing. I want to lie down and sleep as I hear, "Amen, amen, amen."

"You can't get lost. There is only one road," she tells me in the morning.

I'm leaving for a trip along the southern coast. She reaches for the unfurled map in my hand, where I circled Vik, on the south coast, as a possible sleeping place.

"I'm going to circle a community swimming pool I think you will like," she says.

Iceland–a swimming and storytelling place–also feels like home.

May I never forget Iceland's changing weather and windswept landscapes, the closeness of the sun, and the rapid transitions from rain to snow to hail to sunshine. Moss-covered lava fields sprinkled with melting snow. Waterfalls. Glaciers breaking, falling, splashing, and floating. Jagged mountains extending to the ocean, Arctic terns dancing in the azure sky. On this island of fire and ice, I feel like I am on a different planet and at home.

The ground covering the lava fields is golden, green, and squishy. I stop to walk on it, to feel the spring of it.

I pass horses, sheep, and bales of hay. I see houses for elves. I see puffins. I love puffins.

Grief swoops in. The height and smoothness of the mountains amplify it. I pull to the side of the road amid them and am surrounded by what looks like gigantic sleeping stegosauruses. Knowing my parents will never be at the end of the road or the phone line again is unfathomable. The future looks like a black wall I am trying to see around.

I think about how Mom saw Dad's mom and grandma in the room the night before he died, as moving shadow portraits on the walls, and how in her last days, Mom told me she thought Dad would show up, and I answered softly that there was still time. When I told a sister, she shook her head quickly, saying, "Dad would never come and take her away from us."

That made me feel better then.

I remember being with Dad seven years earlier, tidying up the newspapers around his chair. "Do you need any of these?" I asked.

"Only if there is something in there about my parents coming back," he answered.

He was 85.

Accepting I will have to keep them alive inside of me, I pull myself together and drive on. Joy rises again, on its own, in the beauty and wonder, and my son calls from Paris as I skirt the southern coast. "I showed a friend of mine the picture you sent this morning, and she said I have a beautiful mother," he tells me. I know my son feels sad about my aloneness because he told me so, and when I mentioned my concern, he said, "Mom, I am thinking about myself 90% of the time and only worry about you 10% of the time."

It is harder for certain people to see me alone than for me to be alone.

I remember Dad telling me it was harder for other people to watch him and Mom with their disabled son than for them to love and care for him.

I keep driving and moving. France's Massif Central comes to mind in Vik. So does coastal Japan. I check into a comfortable hotel, eat a delicious meal of fish, and admire the elves' houses as I stroll to the cemetery on a hill, where I look for my friend's grandparents' graves which I do not find because I am unaware that a father and daughter do not share the same surname in Iceland. Women have *dóttir* as a suffix on their surnames, and men have *son*. After giving up the search, I stand for a while, enjoying the view of the Atlantic and the dots of lighted homes from the hill.

On the way back to Reykjavík, I stop at the pool my friend circled on the map. I realize I forgot to bring a swim cap. The man at the reception desk offers me a golden one with a sketched tiger's face on the back of it. I swim laps alone in the Icelandic mist, imagining that tiger face bobbing in the water, then sit in the steam room, which looks more like a steam cottage, painted a soft blue. It all makes me feel so clean and smooth, and slick.

"You are the only foreign visitor I ever had that found their way home alone," my friend says when I arrive. "You are a good navigator."

After choir practice, I mention a song I like. "The lyrics are funny," she tells me. "They are about how love will come along one day, and the singer says, 'remember what I said when it does,' but the song never tells us what he said."

I laugh and feel my parents inside of me, laughing with me. I am again lying on the floor nearby them while they kibitz in their chairs, with the door open and a breeze floating through the living room.

On the last morning in Iceland, I go to the neighborhood pool for a couple of hours and sit in the hot pot, then the steam room. I swim laps, then lie back in the shallow pool while the sun, sleet, rain, snow, and light hail take their turns passing over me.

In Paris, I speed write to finish this story that seems never to end–at least until I die–and someone else writes that sentence.

I hope I will be near my son when I go. Please let me have a long, healthy life and a peaceful, gentle death, I pray. Then I pick up a notebook and time-travel a couple of years to the other side of the Atlantic, where I enjoy listening to a diplomat's voice in my bed through a phone.

"I feel no urgency about seeing him, though," I say to a sister later.

"The good thing is you have your eyes wide open," she answers.

A t a café on Place de la Contrescarpe, light is spilling everywhere it can as I enjoy coffee with my son, then writing alone. Then I get up and walk again. This day I will walk for ten hours and write ten-thousand words.

J'écris, assise (French words creep back in, they are on my tongue) in Le Procope, a café and restaurant founded in 1686, which I daresay smells like it (mostly upstairs). A cappuccino and a tiramisu wait on the table near my notebook. A plaque behind me says I am warming the same seat two authors of the United States Declaration of Independence and the first U.S. ambassadors to France did. It's a good one with a view of the street through paned windows, in which the satin fuchsia ankle boots I am wearing are reflected. There is also a view to the door though those entering must make some effort to see this seat.

While American English is subsiding in me, it is difficult to recall the French gender of things. I am always annoyed that I must think about that when vocabulary and grammar are enough to master. Yet I find this assignment of femininity or masculinity to objects fascinating and am curious about the occasional differences between French and Spanish, the two foreign languages I know. Freedom, though, is feminine in both languages.

Gender differences bring to mind an afternoon when my son was 7, and he came home from school and said, "Girls, girls are wild, Mom. Boys are in a cage."

*J**e bave*, these two words repeat in my mind as I walk around Paris, immersed in the architecture, park scapes, food, clothing, art, and jewelry. I stroll rue Vieille du Temple, where my agent's office used to be. With French friends, I eat lunch outside on a terrace with terrible service and beautiful views.

In the Jardin du Palais Royal, a French friend and I drink mint tea in the shade. We talk about her upcoming interview with me in Chicago to promote my first novel. The alley of trees stretching before us sparkles with new leaves. The fountain gushes.

I feel at home as she reminisces about her children as toddlers playing in the sandbox nearby before she and her American husband left Europe.

Finally, I say I must go and do some writing. I walk through the heat, under the Carrousel, cross the Seine, traffic, and so many people, already tired of all that.

Paris, I think, is best in small, intermittent doses.

At Au Rocher de Cancale, I write as I wait for the well-dressed waiter to ask me what I would like. Eyes that meet mine seem startled. I am typing without looking at the keyboard. When I write, I imagine I am playing the piano, making a story and a song. Ancient wisteria blooms hang in hundred-foot tresses from roofs across the street. I am thinking about where I have to go next in this story. To the courtroom. It seems unbelievable that I am sitting in Paris, and the French defendant is living in Iowa when I get to this part.

A father and his two daughters are in front of me. The man turns and asks if it will bother me if he smokes. I say yes. So he doesn't. This impresses me so much that I feel ready to go on.

"I hate the sound of *ex* anything; it sounds like a guillotine," I respond—at a party in my honor in Paris—to a Frenchwoman's question about someone we both know.

She touches my arm and says, "*Tu sais qu'on aime bien la guillotine içi, Marianne.*" This means "you know we like the guillotine here, Marianne." The sentence is even funnier with the name Marianne because Marianne is the symbol of the French Republic, the woman of statues, currency, stamps, and more. She is the goddess of liberty and revolution.

In Paris, after writing hard stuff, I order a noisette with a *café gourmand*.

A noisette is a hazelnut and is also the name for an espresso with a dash of warm frothy milk. The *café gourmand* is a surprise selection of three mini-desserts with an espresso. Because I prefer that with a warm frothy dash of milk, I always specify that I would like the coffee in my *café gourmand* to be a noisette.

Also, when writing about difficult things, a *café gourmand* is sure to help the journey from pain to sweetness.

In Dubuque, during the years of mayhem, a friend says, "Things will settle." Settle how, and are they settled now?

Yes, is an answer that comes in Los Angeles five years later. A strange and funny response amid a pandemic, raging fires, and earthquakes.

People often ask if I will settle in one place.

In Barcelona, seven years after the first sentence on this page, a handsome younger man who likes kissing me says, "But it seems you *are* settled–inside yourself."

It's this, I think, glad he sees this. This is home.

Dubuque, Iowa, is like a David Lynch movie. Well, a few combined: mix *The Short Story* with *Blue Velvet* and a pinch of *Twin Peaks*. Everything looks squeaky clean, with rockers on front porches, children playing on lawns, and kind and decent people like my parents saying hello. Then underneath that, one can find folks sleeping with their friends' husbands and wives, inviting them over for supper while doing so, and calling that behavior sophisticated. Abuse of women and children, a meth crisis, and stolen guns from Chicago sold off trucks on the north end of town where Mom grew up–these things are also under the city's rug. Despite outsider belief that the place is livable only for those who love county fairs, baseball diamonds, drag car racing, and tractor pulls for entertainment, there is a symphony, an art museum, a ballet, and an international film festival.

All of this is less than ten miles from Key West, the rural community I grew up in, up the hill from the farm where my father, his siblings, and their mother were also born and grew up. Up on that hill is where my sizable extended family grew up, enjoying things like riding horses, shooting clay pigeons, hosting bonfires, and playing baseball, football, basketball, tennis, and euchre, among other pleasures. However, sleigh riding down the hill and ducking under the barbed wire fence has seen its day.

In 2012, I know that going back there, I will watch my mother die. I will be surprised to see my marriage die. It makes sense, though, in a way, because I kind of married my mom. Kind of, I stress, and mainly in a bittersweet way. Mom changed over time, however, and Mom gave me a lot. Like life, for starters.

Some people look at me skeptically when I say returning to my childhood home is like a dream after traveling and living in the broader world.

But it is, even though sometimes it looks more like a nightmare.

"Are you back here permanently?" one woman asks.

"I've never really thought of doing anything permanently," I say.

My mother, sitting next to me, nods knowingly.

"The husband takes up too much space in this story, and it is unfair to your story," an editor tells me. "All we need to know about him is that he resists supporting his son and needlessly moves into a homeless shelter."

"I've had enough of the husband," another editor mentions. "You can keep going with this if you want, but you have to know that the more the narrator puts up with him, the less the reader likes her."

And the less she likes and respects herself, I think. The less she is herself.

A few months after Dad dies, Mom says, in a small voice over the phone, "I don't see why if you can teach at the University of Barcelona, you can't come home and teach at a university in Dubuque."

When I hang up the call, I look out the window of my attic sanctuary and wonder if I want to miss the end of Mom's life as I missed Dad's. It is September. I send some e-mails to universities. A couple of them answer, telling me they have no openings, and I receive no response from others.

That winter, my fifteen-year-old son, who loves his American family and month-long visits in Dubuque, who used to plead to live in Iowa after our return from there, asks, "Mom, could I study abroad in Iowa?"

When I tell my sister about this, she offers that he stay with her family and go to high school with his cousin. My husband and I talk to the French school he attends in Sitges and make arrangements for a semester because the French refuse to accept an American academic year in exchange for a French academic year. He will have to catch up when he gets back.

As I prepare to go with my son to help him settle in in July, I receive an e-mail from a university: We had no openings last fall when you wrote. However, a long-time instructor has announced that she is leaving. Would you be interested in teaching three courses in composition this fall?

I'm going to be in Dubuque on Saturday, I answer.

Could you come to my office on Monday? The chairperson responds.

I call and tell Mom, "I have an interview at a university in Dubuque next week."

I hear silence then, her whispers, "Thank you, God."

That's how it was. Mom, then son, calling me home.

"Isn't that below the poverty level?" I ask, after being told the salary for teaching three classes. "And without benefits?"

The person offering me the job shifts in the chair. "It's awful, I know. We'd love to have you, though."

A friend will tell me later that with that salary, one can also get food stamps, which according to her, most adjuncts do.

"Take it; something else will come; you never know where it might lead," a sister says. "That is what Dad would tell you."

"You have to do what you think is right," Mom says, now nervous that if the return is miserable, her answered prayers will be to blame.

"I like it here, Mom," my son says.

"You must do what you will not regret. If you decide to take it, I will come, but I cannot come right away," my husband says on the phone from our Mediterranean home.

I call a friend in California from my cousin's backyard. "I want to come back in many ways, yet I am worried I will go crazy and get fat. The university, though, could introduce me to new people. I'll have to give up the modeling and acting work for a while, but I can finish writing the dissertation here."

"Would you like me to remind you of a conversation we had ten days ago?" my friend asks.

"Please do," I say, pacing the lawn and pausing to slide the grass between my toes. It is the last day of July 2012; the sun bears down, family is inside with the air-conditioning, preparing corn-on-the-cob, tomato salad, and bratwurst. I am thinking of a few longtime friends I still have in town and all the family.

This friend on the phone says, "Ten days ago, I was listening to things from you like: I am tired of living in a foreign country; I am tired of living so far from family, of speaking and dealing with everything in foreign languages, of being a foreigner. I am hearing now that you are being offered what you want and are worried about your weight?"

While I eat at my cousin's table, Mom and an aunt at my sides, I recall a phone conversation with Dad six months before he died, when I'd said, "I can't believe I have been gone almost twenty-five years."

"All I know is it's been a hell of a long time," was his response.

The first fall that I am back and at the cemetery with Mom, I drop, face down, on the grass of Dad's burial ground and lie there for a while. Mom gasps. "Oh my god, honey, you just did me a world of good."

In Sitges, I have two weeks to pack and say goodbye to beloved friends and places. Many tough decisions about what to leave behind have me walking in circles on the western terrace of our rented rooftop duplex in the center of town. Surrounded by honeysuckle, jasmine, and belles de nuit, I take in the beloved views of terra cotta roofs, pine-filled hills, sky, and a sliver of the sea imagining we can live well and surrounded by beauty in Iowa, too, and travel often. Students and the community might enjoy the perspective of a native daughter coming home. They may love having her French architect husband design their buildings and homes. Our son will learn about American culture, history, and literature inside the country instead of in a French school in Catalonia. I want my son to connect with half of his roots more fully. I want him to know what it is like to live in a house on a street in a town where people know his extended family, and he can visit them whenever he likes. They can come to his place for dinner on Sundays, birthday parties, and other celebrations. They can stop in; he can stop in. I sense we can all heal in Dubuque in different ways.

On the eastern terrace, I stare at the palm-filled courtyard and the foothills of the Garraf mountain range on the near horizon. Then I climb the stairs to finish the last couple of tasks that will empty my sanctuary—an embellished garret space behind our bedroom. I lift the sparkling oblong crystals hanging from the window, and flashing rainbows streak on the wall as the sun lowers in the sky and enters the room. I roll up the long narrow Moroccan rug I so often danced on. I stand in the space, looking around, remembering all my work there: translation, editing, and writing—finishing the Master's thesis, the first novel, and the bulk of the doctoral dissertation. While scared about the unknown and thinking about how I wrote myself out of this long, narrow space a friend once referred to as a birth canal, pulsations herald another spontaneous orgasm. One of those mysterious visits coming on strong. This comforts me. Life seems turned on by my move.

I t seems essential to write this. Traveling around the world in my mid-twenties, living the life I dreamed about, magical, mysterious, spontaneous orgasms struck me. I began listening to them and using them as a compass. Sometimes the places where they happened turned out to be significant in my life. Sometimes the people in whose presence I was when arousal appeared were substantial to my creativity and evolution. Sometimes the orgasms goaded a decision, or they congratulated me on one. Arousal became another key to finding my way home. This knowledge that my excitement was an inside job rather than a power another had over me gave me more freedom.

"I hear you are writing a novel about a woman who has spontaneous orgasms," a man told me at a writing conference in Vermont. "Do you know that happens?" he asked as if I didn't.

"I do," I said.

"I am a doctor," he tells me, "and in my country, we insert a little chip near the occipital bone." He touches the back of his neck to let me know where that is. "That stops them."

I shake my head and walk on.

"Why would I want to read about a character like that?" Another man asks. "It means she doesn't need me."

This baffles me. Wanting to be wanted, that I get.

In some research, these orgasms are defined as a disease, and in others, as side effects of some medications. The female orgasm is often presented as something gifted to a woman by someone else.

Playing pool with a couple of guys I knew in Spain, one asked, "How many times have you come in one love-making session?"

I am taken aback by the question. They are surprised by the answer. "Wow, he must be an incredible lover," one says.

"*I* am an incredible lover," I say, then pocket a bank shot.

"Your father wants to talk to you. He's in the bathroom. I'm handing him the phone."

"Mom, wait."

"Your mother showed me that writing of yours. All those pages of orgasms you got there remind me of a joke," Dad says, talking about a manuscript I sent to Mom to get her permission to use some of her information.

"Are you on the toilet?" I ask.

"What's it to you?" he says. "I want to know if this writing of yours will be showing up in my friends' mailboxes?"

"No," I say, knowing he is more concerned about his father's appearance in the story than about the orgasms. "I told Mom not to show you that."

"I imagine you did. By the way, I think it's time you bury the hatchet with your grandfather." He says, talking about his father. "I don't see why anyone needs to know about that."

"I understand what you're saying, Dad. It's hard for me, but you know this kind of thing destroys lives, and I want to show a way not to be destroyed," I say.

"Well, I'm sorry you had to go through that," he says. "Are you there?"

"Yeah. You left me speechless. I have wanted to hear that for fifteen years. Thank you." Another gift writing gave me, that is. "So, tell me, what's the joke?"

"Four people are playing cards, and one of the women keeps sneezing, then giggling. Finally, a guy asks her why she is giggling. 'Oh,' she says, 'every time I sneeze, I have a little orgasm.'

'What's your secret?' one of the women at the table asks.

'Pepper,' she says."

"Dad," I say.

For whatever it's worth:

A month or so before Dad dies, a sister calls and tells me he has been kicked out of the dining room at the nursing home. "What on earth?" I ask.

"He was putting pepper in everyone's water."

Almost a year after Dad dies, I am at a dinner during a conference. The French philosopher leading it sits at my side. It is the night before she will publicly berate me about my presentation referencing the orgasms. During our banter, I am wide-eyed as she playfully lifts the pepper mill from the dinner table and grinds peppercorns into my glass of wine.

"What exactly do you want us to write?" a sarcastic student asks one morning at the end of February. It's 2016. So much has changed in three and a half years.

"Use your imaginations and curiosity," I say, adding as playfully as I can, "and if you are uninterested in curiosity or imagination, I don't know, go and jump off a bridge. For now, though, shut up and write."

A favorite in that class, who sits in front, widens his eyes, "Um, she's gone high flame, folks."

I'm embarrassed now, remembering I said that. I was just so tired of students' unwillingness to learn or think about things.

A sister-in-law's newly widowed brother palms my arm in sympathy at a street party in the summer of 2015 and says, "I've been where you are, and I can tell you, divorce is much worse than death."

Preparing to leave Sitges, repeatedly passing my husband, kicked back with his legs up on his desk, playing a game on the computer, I say, with my arms full of heavy boxes, "I am not leaving you, but since you are not helping me, it looks like I am, and feels like I am."

How many times did I leave in all?

I left him in Osaka, Paris, Hong Kong, and Sitges until I finally left him in Dubuque. Perhaps I was always leaving him.

"You better not write about this," the man I am leaving says near the end of our time together.

"I don't even want to remember this," I say.

Yet I know writing is a way of forgetting.

In a friend's home in the Colorado desert six years later, I look up from editing, wondering whether to keep some of the man's behavior on the page. Outside I see a roadrunner on a pile of smooth rocks in front of a palm tree; the bird is paused and looking off like me.

I am the Road Runner; it dawns on me. He is Wile E. Coyote.

I will write what's necessary and move on.

Leaving the sea was the hardest part. My happiest moments were near it. Morning and evening dives, swimming out until lifeguards blew whistles and raised their hands for me to halt. Treading water at that distant point between the buoys, looking at the village like a postcard. Floating on my back, ears submerged to hear only the sea. Tasting salt on my lips and skin while lying on the sand. Rollerblading, walking, and running along it. Playing racquetball with my husband for hours, then diving in and wrapping my legs around him and floating. Chatting, reading, sketching, playing cards, and lightly touching each other now and again. Playing with our son there, watching him run along the shore, laughing and singing while pushing him on a swing in front of the rolling waves. The school bus stop was on the sea; it was also a joy seeing him skip down the school bus stairs and run toward me with open arms! I can still feel him wrapping those solid little arms around me after I lifted him on the back of the bike, how he pressed his hands and body against my back, holding on as we rode along the shore.

When he was four, and we were walking along the sea, he asked, "What happens when we die, Mom?"

"I don't know. Some people think we get more than one life."

He threw his arms in the air. "Yes! Then I want the same one, Mom!"

When he was 15, we sat in a sunny booth at a Mexican restaurant in Dubuque, just the two of us, on a Sunday afternoon, during that first fall before his father arrived. He was telling me how surprised he was that some classmates had never been to the other side of the river. "I want to raise my kids the way you and Daddy raised me," he said.

That was a relief.

I wonder if he would say those things now. It was good to hear them when I did.

That first week teaching at the university, I stay with Mom in the apartment I saw for the first time two years earlier when arriving for Dad's funeral.

My eyes darted around the room then, looking from face to face–of brothers, sisters, close family friends–looking for him. Mom hugged me and whispered, "Everyone is here but the main man."

It was strange, then, and is now, to see only Mom's name on the door. She had moved into a one-bedroom apartment in the assisted living center near Dad's room in the adjacent nursing home. She told me how Dad looked around in disbelief as he tried to get through in his wheelchair. "What the hell are you doing in a tiny place like this?" he'd wanted to know.

And now I sit in Mom's recliner, remembering my last month with them while watching a light show of rainbows flashing on the wall through crystals I sent to her over the years.

❝I don't know what we would have done without our daughter here," Mom tells the director of the posh assisted living center where they moved a few years earlier, hoping it would be their last move.

It is ten weeks before Dad dies. I wake up on the pull-out couch in the middle of the night, hearing him call my name. As I sit up, the wheels of Mom's walker shake like a tambourine across the kitchen floor as she races to one bathroom to get things out of her, and Dad is stumbling to the other, trying to keep things in. I run back and forth between them. I push the help button Mom points to. Help eventually comes. Then I stay up with both, massaging their feet until they fall asleep.

That day, in a doctor's office with my parents, I'd said, "I think Dad's bowel issues are ruining his quality of life."

"You've got that right," Dad confirmed with visible joy and relief to hear it spoken.

"You're an 85-year-old man, that's part of it, and with the stroke damage, there's nothing much to be done," the doctor shrugged as he said that as if talking about a car.

I wanted to slam that doctor against the wall. I hated the nonchalance and the sitting back and chatting like this was a social visit. I wondered how many dollars that cost. Maybe it was true that nothing could be done, but at least quit bringing the guy in to chat about the hopeless situation is how I saw it. I wondered whether it was appropriate for me to speak. I thought of elder friends and family complaining about other doctors saying similar things and acting similarly about ailments. It looked like elderhood meant no longer being valued as a liver of life, as worthy of healing. I was headed back to Spain soon, and another sister played the medical advisor role. As I wondered what the best thing to do was, the nurse handed my parents each a candy bar and talked to them in a cooing voice like they were toddlers; this, in the face of their misery and approaching separation from each other after 66 years together. I rolled the stool I was on back and away and turned toward the wall to hide the tears rising in me. It felt disrespectful when these people asked Mom if Dad needed more help than she could give him, in front of him, like they were both children. Then they asked me the same question in front of them, putting me in what felt like a potential situation of betrayal. "I think they both need help," I said.

"That hospital stay sure was comfortable," Dad said.

"That's an expensive stay," the doctor said, then smiled.

It was one of the most ridiculous conversations I had ever witnessed. And awful to see amid all the crumbling moments of my parents' lives splitting into Mom, left alone.

A family friend I have known all my life invites me to breakfast the next day. Over pancakes, she says, "You kids have to do something. Your mother can't. And she is going to fight you because that is what she has to do, but you have to get your dad into hospice or a nursing home. Your mom is worn out." After breakfast, she drives me to the nursing home she recommends, and we inquire about availability.

"Dad, do you think it would be a good idea for you to go somewhere now where you could have nurses helping you all the time?" I ask that afternoon when we pause to sit during a walk through the hallways. He taps his cane on the ground as his mother used to and looks out the window toward the horizon and the rolling hills leading home.

"Yes, babe," he says. "I think that is probably what I need."

We avert each other's eyes then. It's so sad. His bearing impresses me deeply. I plan to be like him. I am amazed at how much the heart can break and still keep beating.

That night I tell my sister—the one Dad calls the chief nurse and bottle washer—what he said.

"That is all I need to hear," she says, and I feel like I have sealed his fate. He will move to the nursing home after I leave.

"You'll get a call one day," Dad says, tapping his cane. "Telling you I'm gone."

"Stop," I say.

"But that's the way it will be, babe. I know you'll miss your dear ol' dad."

Eighty-three days later, that call comes. I know it when the phone rings. "He's gone, isn't he?" I say, at home, alone.

"Do you want to talk to him?" my sister says.

"I thought you said he was dead," I answer.

I walk in circles in the living room in front of the fireplace, thanking my father through the phone, picturing him dead in a bed, and then as I realize I am sobbing in his ear, I feel bad and stop. After I hang up, I put on sunglasses and walk downstairs and out into the village to feel my feet walking, to feel like I am going somewhere, anywhere. I call my husband at some point. I wait to tell my son. It's the feast of Sant Joan, and he is with friends at the *Nit del Foc*, the night of fire. Fires along the miles of beach in Sitges. Celebrations. Fireworks in the village.

The last time I see my father alive, we lie together for hours, like spoons. I listen to the struggle of his breathing, bury my face in my sleeve, so he doesn't feel my tears. "I hope you know how thankful I am for this time with you," he says.

It's been a month filled with precious and funny moments despite the hard ones. He wants to come to the airport. All caretakers disapprove. It feels wrong to insist, so I say goodbye to him at home with Mom in the other room. I hold his face and then run my hand through his hair. He had beautiful hair. I kiss him on the forehead.

"I'd like to see your plane taking off into the sky," he says.

I have no idea how I am able to walk away from him, then Mom, calmly, even to back out of the door, waving and blowing kisses. It seems essential to spare Dad my tears. Earlier in the week, when I helped him do some exercises and pressed him back up against the wall, he stood straight and tall as he used to for a moment. I cried at seeing him looking down into my face like he used to. "Now, don't do that, don't cry like that. I can't stand that," he said.

"Of course, I said, wiping my tears, only imagining how hard it was for him to no longer be able to stand up tall.

Eight years earlier, I'd said goodbye to him in the hospital, where he had just gotten out of intensive care after suffering a stroke during a heart valve replacement. I stayed at the hospital with him and Mom for two weeks. Then, I was standing by his bed with a suitcase in my hand and a frown on my face. "Don't look for any sympathy from me," he said.

I turned toward Mom, who looked into my eyes and whispered, "Be brave."

"I'll call you," I said to Dad.

"I'll be right here by the phone," he answered.

During those first months in Dubuque, I rent an upstairs room—with a screened-in porch perched above a back garden under an oak tree in a beautiful Arts and Crafts house—from a Trinidadian poet. I love the pistachio and white tiled kitchen floor, the crannies built into walls to hold rotary telephones, the bathtub with feet, the old-fashioned plumbing fixtures, and the glass doorknobs. It feels like living in either of my grandmas' houses. "This is the street your dad's grandparents lived on, his dad's parents," Mom tells me when I drive her there in my sister's car. I like imagining Dad as a boy walking the street I now live on.

My son is living with my sister and her family. The university and Mom's place are within walking distance. I teach in the mornings and work on the dissertation in the afternoons. I like to walk down to the river, then along it, at sunset. I love autumn's green and golden beauty, the crisp blue enormous sky, the wide winding river, tall, jagged limestone bluffs, and smooth driftwood on the sand. I love the cable car ride back up the bluff, sitting on a wooden bench seat in a wooden car, my eyes following the southern bend of the Mississippi.

During moments of engaging conversation with students, I enjoy teaching. "There are usually a couple of good students in a classroom of twenty," a colleague tells me. A negative handwritten evaluation of me by a first-year student reads *Standards way to* [sic] *high.*

I see family on the weekends. Sometimes on Friday nights, I meet friends for an Old Fashioned somewhere. In Dubuque, I can order a Southern Comfort Old Fashioned without flack.

I join the local Writers Guild.

I spend hours laughing and dancing to Calypso music at home with the poet and her sister, who also lives there.

"Wow, this is like SoHo with nice people," I say at an artsy party in an old warehouse downtown.

"I loved talking to you when you first got back," a friend tells me a year later, "you sounded so happy."

A professor at another university says, "We don't have any open positions, but would you like to join a monthly coffee group we call Second Saturdays?"

The first time I go, I meet a woman who never returns. "My grandfather probably delivered you," she says, looking at me. "He delivered almost all the babies of your generation." She speaks the name of the doctor who delivered the brother I never knew.

And I hear Mom telling me, "I was in labor for twenty-three hours, on all fours on that table, screaming in pain. 'What if we all get down on our knees and pray?' the doctor said. One of the two BVM sisters in there with me–she had kept telling him to go and get someone else to help–left the room and came back with a specialist and forceps. They got him out. The umbilical cord was wrapped around his neck. Ten days later, I stood in front of the picture window, crying, saying, 'My baby does not blink.' We took him back to the doctor and were told our baby was blind, deaf, and dumb and had cerebral palsy. The cord, they said, cut off the circulation to his brain. I knew he could hear because he laughed when I talked, sang, and told him stories."

He lived for almost nine years like a helpless infant. Seven years after his birth, Mom gave birth to a healthy baby girl, then four more children–five healthy babies in five years. And another one almost six years after that, when she was 42. I am the sixth of these seven children. All delivered by a different doctor than the first.

After that coffee group, I visit Mom and tell her I met the granddaughter of the doctor who delivered my eldest brother.

Her eyes fill with what seem like faraway images.

"Well," she says, then takes a deep breath, "it's not her fault."

"Do you want him to come to Iowa?" a friend asks about my son's father.

I stare out at the oak, dropping golden leaves like snow. The scent of a nearby charcoal grill wafts through the screen. I lie down on the rug. It is easier for me to think on my back. "I feel like I have to give it a chance," I say.

D eep pleasures abound that first fall:
      watching my mother laugh;
      listening as she asks people for their family names, then speaks of tribal connections;
      the sparkle in her eyes when she asks, "Did you know my husband?";
      hearing Dad's name and stories about him;
      living with warm, fun, and smart sisters;
      being near my own;
      walking everywhere;
      rekindling relationships;
      recognizing new friends;
      watching my son attend a Homecoming dance;
      driving to Madison and sitting on the lake with a friend made in Paris, looking out at the sailboats, feeling like we are in Bavaria;
      celebrating my birthday on a riverboat with the women in my family;
      reading from the manuscript of my first novel at the university;
      a student shaking my hand after that reading saying, "I feel like I am at a real university now";
      a fellow citizen writing to tell me she marveled at my writing and reading;
      a student writing to tell me I inspired her;
      a prize-winning feminist author coming to town to read in the same series as I, making me feel I am moving toward the big leagues as a group of us dine and drink with her afterward in yet another renovated building on the river;
      twirling leaves emit their nutty scent as they fall and dance across the street;
      the river and a paddleboat;
      the damp greengoldgrayness of fall;
      bands of salmon sunset above Illinois bluffs;
      vines dancing like ferns in the wind on brick houses.
      Dreaming, I am, and aching for my father and the sea.
      Do not think of the Spanish shores. Write–a new friend sends me this message.
      A train gathers momentum and slithers along the river, bellowing, maintaining constancy, relentless to its destination.

We attend a lively party at the art museum when my husband arrives. It is a glittery night, shining in that way new beginnings can. "Look at this fun life we can have here for a while," I am saying.

He likes parties. He seems much less interested in looking for work.

The bluff top is untouched after deep snow blankets the roll of the land. Congealed flakes hang from evergreens like drippings on a sandcastle, sparkling in the sun. I walk into the white woods. Bald eagles circle. Cardinals rest alert on branches. Below, patches of ice form on the surface of the river. Eagles dive into the churning water near the dam. A message from Sitges appears on my phone: *This move of yours is serendipity at work. Do not forget that.*

Sleigh-riding with my son and husband, I laugh until I cry as we fly down hills.

"Do you feel at home there?" A friend asks.

"I wonder if I will ever feel at home anywhere," I answer.

I hold my heart when I learn apartment and house rental prices in Dubuque are similar to those in Sitges within steps from the Mediterranean. A friend says it is because most people live in the homes they own in the city. I see an ad for a two-bedroom on Main Street and imagine a walking life, a downtown community like when I was a girl.

The top floor of an early-twentieth-century brick apartment building facing a park and a beautiful Victorian mansion becomes our newest home.

The mansion across the street was a funeral home for decades. Every day I look out the window and remember my father's parents' wakes there.

I like the skyline of steeples, the gold dome of the courthouse, and the white clock tower.

I love being in my hometown in a new way.

Walking on deep ice-covered snow is like walking on a vast crème brûlée.

There are reprieves of forty-five-degree weather in mid-January, a brief advertisement for spring. A friend asks me to speak about the eros portion of my dissertation work at Valentine's Day dinner at her home.

I say yes.

I look out at bare branches, count the days until spring, and wonder what the downtown roofs are made of. Some seem like slate roofs in Paris.

It is below zero Fahrenheit. My hands stiffen while scraping ice and snow off the windshield.

Driving back down the steep hill after dropping my son at school, the same high school I attended, I pull over to watch the sun break the horizon and then rise above the city and river.

These moments touch me, this coming around again, this chance to see this beauty anew and to share knowledge gleaned on my journey in the place I once only wanted to leave.

One afternoon at the city library, while I descend the swirl of marble stairs under the skylight dome I marveled at as a girl, a librarian calls my name. She introduces herself and says, "I have heard about you. Would you come and speak or read from your work?"

"I would love to," I say.

The editor of a local newspaper magazine calls. "I think your experiences are so interesting, and if you are okay with it, I would like to interview you for a story. *Coming Home* will be the title," she says.

I accept.

How is it that sometimes, after pain settles in, we forget the joy?
I enjoy watching a warehouse district property owner ask my husband for his renovation vision. Sun streams through the office windows, lighting the palms and giant philodendrons climbing the brick walls of the former factory. I imagine Dad watching and shedding grace on the moment as I imagine my husband part of significant transformations in the city.

The best thing I hear at the New Year is my son saying, "I think this experience in Iowa is going to be a very important one in my life, Mom."

The last summer in Dubuque, I open the car windows to feel the gusts of wind and hear the cracks and slices of thunder, to listen to the waves the wind creates on the river, the swoosh of the trees.

At a brother and sister-in-law's, I say, "I did a count and saw I can make it on a very tight budget, and then I realized I forgot to put food on the list."

"You can eat here," my sister-in-law says.

It is hot in January, that first winter, with the sun gushing through the windows surrounding the library's airy glass-floored loft. I move from chair to chair to keep it shining on me as I work on the critical exegesis of the composite dissertation I will present in July.

A 370-page novel I wrote is one part, and the other is a 100-page critical exegesis on eros, voice, and wound. I am using these three themes as a map to wholeness, engaging the plot and characters of the novel with the work of European and American scholars.

Sometimes my head feels like it is in a vise.

"Writing a dissertation is a beautiful process, do not break your head over it, enjoy it," one supervisor writes from Australia.

"You do not need to claim that your novel is important," a supervisor from Barcelona adds. "Use it to say that there can never be too many of this story."

It's challenging articulating how wounds silence the wounded, how lack of voice weakens eros, and how the world would be different if everyone voiced their injuries precisely. How would it change the way we use the power of eros? As I struggle and ponder answers, the librarian sets a cup of coffee on the table near my laptop, as she often does, smiles, and says, "Carry on."

The novel is a story of a young woman from Iowa who becomes an international model to travel the world. While doing so, she unwittingly is healing a wound she only sees once she returns to the place where it was inflicted. It's weird and fitting to conclude the writing about it in my hometown.

What happens when a grandfather a girl loves and trusts, who loves her, wounds her? What happens to that girl after she keeps quiet because telling her parents and others about that wound would hurt them more than she thinks it has hurt her? How does this affect how the girl grows, trusts, and becomes herself? How does it affect the way she constructs her life? These are the questions I ponder in the dissertation.

Years of looking at the novel and the exegesis and the girl and young woman I once was as a character help me see that more than a spontaneous orgasm story, the book I have written is a girl-gets-wounded-girl-loses-herself-girl-gets-herself-back story.

I trace that path and see how writing and the love of it lead me to Master's and PhD programs.

At the university, I write a novel and discover that it is about a wound.
Mom, who helped me voice that wound, calls me home.
A university at home offers me a job.
Writing about the wound leads me home.
My interest in what ignites me leads me home.
Writing leads me home.

I drive, swerving in the deep snow, wondering if I will make it to the university or get hit. I make it, then face an eight-a.m. classroom of empty stares. When no one speaks, I have them write for ten minutes. These daily writings become my favorite things to read. I like the sound of twenty pens moving across paper. I pass out tissues to those sniffling, insisting on nose-blowing.

Sometimes at night, I dream I am swimming in the Mediterranean.

After my son leaves for college, alone in the house, I hear children laughing and shouting while leaving school across the street. A breeze and golden light pass into the bedroom. News of another stall in the divorce process arrives. Resting on the bed, I see a fluttering blue-and-white checked cloth over a table in the center of that sunny garden along the Loiret in autumn. A table set with *pâté en croûte, soupe de poireaux*, Emmental, and olives. The early days. Without computers, telephones, or television. Just a radio, guitar, fireplace. A rowboat. A payphone on the other side of the bridge.

"Imagine the pencil you keep in your hand as you teach is a magic wand and see yourself casting sparkles and seeds and let the students do their part, receiving them," a practical visionary I often consult suggests when I express my frustration with teaching people who seem uninterested in learning.

"I'll whittle you a wand," a nephew offers after he listens to me telling his mother about that.

"I don't know how you can see anything. Do you know where we are going? Where are we? Are you sure we are going the right way?" Mom asks.

"My eyes are thirty-six years younger than yours. I am taking you home a different way. I may have been gone a long time, but I have been back a while, and anyway, I still remember where things are."

At the pool, I see a high school friend's husband, a kind person. His wife knows me better than he does, and his family knows mine. After he tells me things the man I left has said to him, I tell him I want to move away. "It would be good to be around people who do not know my story," I say as I dip my toes in the water to test the temperature.

He looks up at me. "But it's a good story," he says.

On bluffs above the Mississippi, near a pool on a stone patio between a chimney and lounge chairs, a new friend introduces me to people at a wine tasting. The host is playing the guitar and singing. The hostess grew up in the Mississippi Valley and married a foreigner, as I did, then lived in Bath, England, for about as long as I lived in Europe. "I used to hang out at the post office to meet people," she tells me, and we share the first of many laughs.

It's so good to hear myself laugh. It is a strange thing to be devoid of laughter for what seems a long time.

I am surprised and pleased to receive a compliment from a handsome man my age who used to tease me when we were 13. "You look marvelous in that color, darling. Red suits you."

It's Valentine's Night at our mutual friends' farm, where I feel flexible, nervous, and prepared to talk about eros. A small group drinks Prosecco and eats almonds around the island bar in the kitchen while others chat in the adjacent open living room.

The table is set for ten, and I am seated in the center. Candlelight and silverware flash as people raise delicious food to their mouths. Each glance out the window is filled with bright snow under a full moon, and I am thinking: How to talk about sex in an intimate roomful of wives and husbands, some of whom I barely know?

After I recite the novel's prologue, there is a moment of silence around the table. My heart pounds as we move to the living room.

I sit next to the fire; my husband sits next to me, the others form a circle that feels like a posse, and I brace myself for the comments sure to come. I remind myself to take my time and to keep my voice as steady, clear, and melodic as possible.

In my hand is a draft of a section of my dissertation and an edited draft of a talk I gave at a conference on eros in Canada a couple of years back. I take a deep breath and begin the presentation. "Associating eros with only love and sexuality and the desire to mate and copulate does a significant disservice to love, sex, and self-construction," I say, then look up from the page. I already see bodies getting straighter and backing away. "Erotica, which Angela Carter refers to as the porn of the elite, is widespread in media, films, literature, and society. Eros is constantly peddled to the human being in one form or another. Eros is consumed, even colonized, by exploiting it for profit. Rilke writes that people squander the pleasure of a sexual experience by using it as a stimulant and distraction instead of exalting it, considering it sacred. He asks why we do not belong to God from this point?" Here, I open my hands, which I have already begun to use in emphasis with the word *exalting*. I look at the former priest in the room. He meets my eye, present and expressionless. I go on. "A current best-selling trilogy, labeled erotic, is about an older male millionaire luring a young woman into a sadomasochistic relationship. Is this not patriarchy?" I ask, looking around the room again, my hand in the air as if

I am holding patriarchy in it. Some faces eye me warily. "Bell Hooks' theorizes that it helps to eroticize domination when one cannot change it," I say, pause, and shrug. Then I state my overall thesis, "I suggest that it is through the command of one's own life that eros is powerfully aroused."

Some folks lean in now.

I quote Judith Butler, "'Our willingness to become undone in relation to others constitutes our chance of becoming human.'" After a pause to separate her words from mine, I speak again. "The sensation of becoming undone, losing control, or being beside oneself that often accompanies the arousal of eros carries the possibility of recognizing vulnerability. If we consider the Hegelian tradition, which claims that all desire is at base a desire for recognition, one can ask what recognition one desires from the other through eros. In other words, is one's desire to be seen by the other a reflection of how one would like to see oneself? Why demand another's effort instead of one's own in that endeavor?" I look at the husbands and wives. Legs uncross, feet go to the floor. The academic language is unusual for this setting. I move on to popular culture. "Norah Jones singing 'like a flower waiting to bloom, like a light bulb in a dark room [...] I'm just sitting here waiting for you to come home and turn me on"—a blatant example of ignorant emotional dependency—topped the charts in France, Canada, and the U.S. as recently as the last decade."

I notice a woman crossing her arms tightly, hugging herself. Maybe she likes the song. I do not. I look for a more familiar face, and with warmth in her eyes and a lift of her chin, she encourages me to go on. I take a sip of water and then say, "Classic story endings of marriage and motherhood representing female fulfillment persist, despite new stories being told," I am reading again from the papers in my hands, now slightly trembling. "Women have been, and still are, often denied, or discouraged to take on, the role of creator of their individual lives. Men are also victims of patriarchy as they are taught to be closed, invulnerable, and to sacrifice love for honor."

I look around the room. One man is rubbing his forehead. Another stretches his chest. I move into the discussion of *Lucy, go see*. "The word orgasm is used only once in the entire novel because it is what is most important about it is what is revealed through the female subject's mysterious, spontaneous experience of it rather than the experience itself. Most of the research literature on this experience is written by men—about women—and these men treat the experience as a disease and a spectacle." I notice a woman on the far side of the room raises her eyebrows.

"Jacques Lacan, though he inferred more than female sexual pleasure when using the term jouissance, did mention a sexual jouissance women are silent about that has nothing to do with men, yet he left his source unmentioned in his seminar on feminine sexuality and the limits of love and knowledge. He also states, "There is a jouissance that is hers, that belongs to that "she" [...] about which she herself perhaps knows nothing if not that she experiences it – that much she knows.""

I pause to take a breath, then carry on dramatizing Lacan's words as if speaking and gesticulating for him here on the farm. "It is widely stated and argued that orgasm is not what Lacan means by jouissance, yet he refers to Saint Teresa in ecstasy and points to her statue in Rome by Bernini, asking, 'What is she getting off on? It is clear that the essential testimony of the mystics consists in saying that they experience it but know nothing of it. What we want to know–in what constitutes feminine jouissance, insofar as it is not wholly occupied with man, and even insofar, I will say, as it is not, as such, at all occupied with him–what we want to know is the status of the Other's knowledge.'" Reading this, I feel the impulse to raise my hand high and exclaim *I'll give you the status of my knowledge!* But I resist and return to the language of my work.

"This dissertation offers a status of at least one Other's knowledge on this "unknowable" issue, eros. Eros brings us to the limits of ourselves, to the limits of knowledge itself, opening the possibility of connection to the world. This thesis suggests that those people and places within whose presence eros is aroused share a mutual involvement in the construction of ourselves and our lives, a creative activity perhaps mistaken for and damaged by the sexual," I say, then take a drink of water.

People seem interested enough or are polite enough, anyway, to feign it. One woman shifts her body away from the person next to her and then straightens her back. As I wonder how outrageous what I am doing is, I keep on. "The novel *Lucy, go see.* plays out how this creative energy can be used in ways that revive rather than consume, leading to thriving interdependent relationships instead of consuming dependent connections, showing how the constitution of one's subjectivity leads to the possibility of two autonomous subjects in one relationship. As the protagonist acquires the strength to recognize and contain vulnerability, she lives a life of continual becoming, engendering relationships based on shared human-beingness, rather than supposed antagonistic genders." My friend lifts her head and smiles at me.

This both reassures me and makes me realize how uneasy I am. I remind myself to slow my speech. Taking a breath, I begin the following passage. "Considering the novel's plot thread following the abuse of eros, the novel can be read as an allegory for the coming home to roost of the patriarchal religious worldview's distortion of the life force. By creating rules to control women and govern sexual relations, which are the life force, the patriarchal religious world puts a vital old widower—the grandfather and crowning member of the family hierarchy—in a position of abusing the lowest and thus most vulnerable member, his granddaughter, to find release for the arousal of eros, understood narrowly within him. Therein, a sacrifice of love, the traditional sacrifice in the patriarchal story, is evident, but the traditional benefit of honor is reversed to shame."

I am mainly trembling inside as I approach the conclusion. "The novel exposes how hierarchal regulations on sex, operating in a submissive/dominant binary, distort intimate relationships between sexes, thus depicting how patriarchy impedes the cultivation of sexual agency in general and female sexual agency in particular. By suggesting that humans (in this case, the dominant male and the seductive female) are responsible for arousing the other (as the victim is often blamed in the case of sexual abuse incidents), society has created the belief that it is the other that is the subject of one's desire, rather than the self. In the words of the narrator of *Lucy, go see.*—'She could take responsibility for her desire more clearly and joyfully, understanding that it wasn't something that happened *to* her but came from or through her. She could use it constructively instead of always thinking of it as something from outside that she had to submit to or conquer. It was becoming clearer and clearer that it was the way she loved, more than was loved, that turned her on.'" When I look up, I notice the woman who presumably likes the Norah Jones song looking at me sideways.

I drink more water and continue. "Lucy Pilgrim's experience of the arousal of eros as a personal compass of her territory leads her to question what eros—life—wants to show her and why. Because she links the arousal to creation, and thus to creativity, she asks what can be created with this arousal, instead of what or who can be consumed by it."

I search for an understanding face trying not to focus only on the women or the same person each time, then say, "The female subject, Lucy, eventually comes to the realization that she is an agent of eros more than a possessor of it, as Rilke himself allowed when he admitted that it did not belong to us. Yet his questions persisted, 'Why are we not set amid what is most mysteriously ours? Why have they made our sex homeless instead of making it the place for the festival of our competency?...it is from this deepest of all events that we come forth and have ourselves the center of our ecstasies in it.'"

Here I pause to look candidly at everyone. People seem as surprised that I can talk about this there and then with them as I am.

I only have a sentence left. "The novel offers a vision of freedom through eros, a possibility of coming home to oneself at the edge of the limits of knowledge, where we all live, consciously or unconsciously."

I place the pages on my lap and say, "Thank you for your attention. I am open to questions and comments."

One woman shakes her head, saying, "I cannot relate to this at all."

It feels intrusive to ask why so I say nothing.

The friend who liked to tease me when we were 13 speaks. "You mention Rilke. Do you know how messed up he was? Do you take that into account?"

"I realize discrepancies exist between what he idealized and what he lived. I see that often."

He sits back. "I have just never heard anyone writing or talking this way about sex."

"Maybe she is the first," my husband interjects.

"Is this story about you?" the teasing friend asks.

I stiffen and ask, "Why do you want to know?"

"Well, I guess because it is a way to know you better," he says.

"Fiction is a sort of veil to play with," I say. "Also, it is a way to protect privacy. This question of whether it is the life of the writer is like prying. It is rude. I would never dare to ask an author this."

The hostess shoots up in her seat. "But why protect? Why not just put it out there? Why not just drop the veil and go for it? Why protect those who do not deserve it? Isn't it time to say the way things are?"

She is a dear friend; she knows this story is about me. I answer, "I hesitate to drop the veil for many reasons, granted I know the veil is thin. I am willing to tell the truth in some places, like here and now, but writing about my sexuality is much easier than speaking about it. I am also concerned about the novel being classified as an abuse novel, limiting it in that way. Fiction is attractive for its playfulness, and I rarely feel playfulness in this kind of truth."

My eyes follow one face to the next, some look at me gently, and some avert their eyes. The woman before me says, "Your energy seems very dense right now."

I sigh.

Her husband rubs his brow, looks at me, and asks, "Do you feel safe here?"

I breathe, then speak. "I have a tough time with the question about whether my life is on the page, and I try to understand why people want to know. Fiction is often truer than a memoir, for example. And memoir is a sort of fiction; memories are stories we tell ourselves, after all. Perhaps I could use the response I've heard another writer use, 'The parts you think are true probably are.'"

"I think that is the best answer," the woman who commented on my energy density says. "Your energy changed when you said that. You look better now."

Because I say nothing in response, we disperse and move toward the island in the kitchen. I am riled. One woman who said nothing in the presentation and was somewhat out of my view says, "People love to dissect artists. Get used to it."

"You just had the dinner party I would love to have," I overhear, then turn to see the person who could not relate to what I was saying telling the hostess goodnight.

The hostess calls the following day to apologize for her intensity and insistence on taking off all protection. I accept her apology with love and carry on with my work.

The entire dissertation must be presented to the doctoral committee in three months. Reading it aloud helped me see some of the clunks in it. I move away from eros to the section on voice, where I write about the mother's voice as the most absent in literature and how its presence can change our world.

The sun burns through the cold pearly February sky, turning the city into a pointillist painting.

After working for a while, I drive Mom to the river to see eagles circling above the bluff. I stop to watch one perched in a pine. I tell myself to be patient. I, too, am perched.

Home in the Iowa kitchen, wondering what to cook, I hear pounding on the front door and open it to a wide-eyed brother. "Where the hell have you been? Mom has the family out looking for you. She is scared out of her mind that your husband has done something to you."

"I was in a lawyer's office. I had my phone off. I'm okay. Why does she think he has done something to me?"

"He went to her place this afternoon and said you weren't answering his calls or messages, and he thought you had run away."

"What??"

"Are you hungry? Want to go to Happy's?" my brother says.

How sweet it is to have a big brother knocking on the door and taking me to a place called Happy's the night before a lawyer will drive me to the courthouse to end my marriage, I think, as I nod, grab a coat, then call Mom on the way to assure her I am okay.

"I hear there is much activity on Facebook," my brother says at the bar.

"I left Facebook," I say.

He smiles. "Isn't it peaceful?"

The following day, a frigid one with bright sun, and snow everywhere, riding alongside the lawyer on the bluff high above the frozen river, I blurt, "I can't believe I worked so hard for so little," knowing I am talking about much more than money.

After the awful and brief court experience, I drive on county back roads, then park next to a nature center path. The phone rings before I get out of the car. Mom is frantic. "Where are you? Are you okay? Is he hurting you?"

"I am at the nature preserve. I need to take a walk. I'm fine and alone."

"Come here right now. How do I know that he is not in that car with you, and you are just saying he isn't?"

"Mom. Gosh. What's going on? I need to be alone for a while. I will call and come as soon as I can. Don't worry."

"You better be telling me the truth," she says, without telling me that he went to her place after the courthouse and upset her so much he was asked to leave.

Messages from the diplomat who has been wooing me for months, telling me I am now free to marry him, stun me. I leave them unanswered.

After walking, I join friends in a café for a glass of wine. Once home, I call Mom to reassure her I am fine and want to sleep, which I do.

Mom is in a terrible mood when I arrive at her place after returning from a weekend in Madison with my son. She is pushing her walker around like a weapon and fuming about how her kids are happy and carefree, going to places without her.

"I'm here now, Mom," I say.

A Valentine's card and envelope with familiar handwriting look like they have been thrown onto the table. I pick up the card and read Mom's former son-in-law's declarations of affection, the list of what he considers her and her children's wrongdoings and unfair treatment of him, an assessment of how much he has done for her, and finally, a proclamation of how hurt and offended he is, and above all, undeserving of the recent request that he check in with the main desk upon arrival so they can call her and ask if she is up for visitors.

I have no interest in talking about this stuff with Mom. Keeping myself together, keeping my job, and helping my son and Mom—these are the priorities. She watches me slip the card into my fanny pack to get it out of her sight.

"Wanna go for a drive, Mom?" I ask.

"I'd love to, honey," she says.

And off we go.

I think a lot about silence as a voice, as a choice, as a speechless voice. Unspeakable silence.

An administrator's wife's lip curls when I tell her how much adjuncts are paid.

"There is something I don't understand," I say to one of the secretaries. "Everyone who knows I teach here tells me how wealthy this university is, how many large gifts it receives, so why is this salary below the poverty level?"

"Oh, that's because the donors specify that they want their money to go to buildings with their names on them," she tells me.

"Did you know all those donors pay for campus erections in their names?" I ask a colleague who shares an office with me.

He chuckles.

Instructed to be "intentionally intrusive" with my students, I call or send them e-mails to ask how they are when they miss class. I receive no responses.

Cut the crap, I think, is the best lecture for writing classes. Three words. One three-second lecture. I give it to myself often. Easier said than done, I know.

The day I discover the missing voice in the novel is the voice of the wound, it sets me back on the couch. I stare out the window at the widow's walk on top of the funeral home, thinking about how I had consistently called the novel a coming to voice instead of a coming of age, and I thought it was Lucy who needed to find her full voice. However, tracing her voice throughout the novel, I see it clearly and firmly from the first page.

It is not until Lucy breaks a decade-long silence about her grandfather's abuse that she can see how her trust, innocence, and sacred sense of sexuality are wounded. This is when she sees her vulnerability and that she is a victim. This word would make her squirm.

I see now that the novel is more about the coming to voice of the wound than the coming to voice of the young woman, though they are inseparable.

Resisting the idea of a "victim novel" is impossible now. "We are all wounded," I say aloud, alone at home. "We are all victims at some point or another. Shame about that keeps us stuck."

I think about the insulting name-calling—*what a victim!*—and how it perpetuates the position—re-victimizing a person—and distracts attention from the trespasser.

When my husband returns from Paris, he will hand me a book I requested, Hélène Cixous's *Entretien de la blessure,* and I will read her poetic declaration that all literature springs from a wound, as do our treasures. Freedom from illusion is a precious one I've just stumbled upon.

Snowflakes flutter. I see mimosas blooming in Sitges.

I go for a drive and end up at the cemetery.

Standing on the icy snow at Grandpa's, Grandma's, and Dad's graves, looking at Mom's name and birthdate etched in front of a hyphen, all ready for her death date to come next, I turn toward the brother I never met's small stone nearby, then walk around all the graves, creating a large heart with boot prints. It feels a little silly but also sweet and fun.

Then, I drive to meet the new friend I feel I've known all my life at a winery near the river. While telling stories, we drink wine and eat charcuterie, and laugh. Afterward, we walk in the snow admiring the full moon on the Mississippi, still storytelling as we stand on the train bridge and then crump along the tracks.

S nowfall and wind create a whipped cream frosting on the bluffs, rooftops, cars, and porches.

I am thinking about the poverty of imagination in the classrooms. The No Child Left Behind Act is responsible for pressuring teachers to teach students to a test, I am told, thus hindering the development of imaginations.

Advertising for universities on the radio is new to me. American universities have become businesses, and students have become clients in the twenty-five years I was away.

Silent worry for my son in this American educational system keeps me up at night.

The snowflakes are errant.

I sketch a steeple and the flags waving from it: the United States flag and the Iowa flag, which uncannily resembles the French flag.

August. 2016. Thunder rumbles and rain pours; I wake in the wee hours with an acrid stomach and a racing mind. "There is nothing there, nothing," I whisper to myself, and the burning in my stomach relaxes with my breath.

How to talk about that feeling of nothing at the center of life? *No thing.* To find peace in that.

B are branches look like fingers reaching from a grave, trembling in the wind.

My godmother, who came to Iowa from Europe as a GI's bride in the 1940s, waves her hand and then wraps her arm around Mom's shoulders. "Oh, could *we* write a book! Oh my god, what we went through."

Both were newlyweds in the mid-twentieth century in Dubuque, both mothers of disabled children, of many children.

"I love that you chose a foreign godmother for me," I tell Mom, then hug them both.

M ice scurry into and around our home. The landlord says he will bring sticky traps. Little do I know I will have to drown the little critters–still alive, stuck, and trembling in the traps–in the sink each morning, then drop their corpses in a plastic bag to toss in the back alley trash.

As a kindergartener, I excitedly ran toward the idling station wagon carrying envelopes for my grandmothers and mother to fill with coins so I could be part of sending a mouse to college for cancer research.

Now, look what I'm doing to them.

My husband is in Paris, visiting his mother. When he returns, he will refuse to help with mouse removal.

The rain wears away the snow as I read more about the importance of caring for our wounds, tending to them–instead of obliterating or ignoring them–and caring for the treasures within them.

Blessure, a French word for wound.

Tu m'as blessé means you have hurt me.

When I say or hear it in French, it sounds like "you have blessed me."

This juxtaposition of wounding and blessing strikes me.

I look up the etymology in English and see it begins with the word *blood* and evolves into *bliss.*

"You know how they used to like to scare kids? Your dad scared the dickens out of me once, sending me outside to get some kindling for the fire, then throwing a wolf's skin over himself and jumping out in front of me from behind the woodpile," my mother's cousin is telling Mom and me.

"I was afraid of Grandpa," I say.

"I never saw anybody talk to their dad as mean as your mother did," Mom's cousin says, then looks at her. "Once we got into high school, you just ripped him apart."

Mom looks away, nodding.

I say, "I am sure she had her reasons."

Her cousin and his wife look at me with surprise. "He was such a good man," his nephew says.

Mom is pressing her lips together.

I want to tell them the story, but it's hers. She permitted me to tell part of it in my first novel, but here, it's hers to tell.

Knowing both my grandfathers hurt children they loved and were loved by makes me wonder how much trauma is hiding in the family tree.

Making love. Why is it called that? Does it come from making love out of sex? I think so.

She holds people accountable is written on a student evaluation of my teaching.

I wonder aloud why some students are so disrespectful to a male colleague who tells me, "Part of the problem is you're a woman."

Being a woman is a problem; this still haunts me, this sentence: a complex problem to solve, that one.

Another male colleague says, "They always want to hurt the prettiest doll."

I amp up efforts to be hired by a different university, where an interesting woman alchemist chairs the humanities department.

In the following months, she will offer me a job, asking if I would like to teach French, English Composition, and Survey of Women's Literature in the fall. The monthly salary is over double what I made the first year back and comes with benefits and my own office.

"That's what I regularly made in a day of modeling or acting," I tell a cousin.

"You can't think about it that way," she says.

I know that. So, I don't.

February 2016. The day before the much-delayed court appearance, I schedule a three-hour massage–accepting whoever is available at the massage school.

"I'm Patience," the massage therapist says as I enter the room. Life has a way of giving us what we need, I think.

After the deep and wonderful relaxation, I go to the hair salon, and a sweet woman washes and styles my hair; then I head to the kind acupuncturist's office, and he places needles where I need them. The cheerful waitress at the Europa Café smiles and says, "You smell so peaceful," when I walk in.

As I eat, the lawyer calls. "I have heard from the judge, and unless a mediation happens, the case will be delayed again. I found someone to do it. I'll call the defendant and inform him. Be there at 4:30."

Then a faraway friend calls to see how I am. "I only asked for some support for our son. Nothing else. He is asking me for spousal support, health insurance, and half of my retirement, and refuses the support for our son," I tell her.

"Sounds like someone has given up all rights to not being written about," she says.

At the mediation, the lawyer looks at the defendant and asks, "So what we are talking about here is willful impoverishment?"

And withheld concealed wealth, I want to add, but I like her term so much I grunt.

The defendant tilts his head in my direction, "She's furious."

"I think she is probably also hurt that you are unwilling to commit to supporting your son."

This lawyer helps me a lot with her language.

Walnut leaves swim through the sky like tiny golden minnows on these final days of my last summer in Dubuque. Most of the oak leaves are still green, wrinkling high on the branches, dancing in the lapis sky under a wispy cloud outside the open windows of the long room upstairs. The smell of solid sun oozes from neighborhood rooftops. A butterfly flits, and a hummingbird pokes its beak into the red cypress vines I planted. I participate in a family constellation session via video call with the visionary.

Constellation work considers all family dysfunction a matter of misplaced loyalties causing stagnation over generations. The aim is to reveal what might need to be seen and said to restore harmony and fluidity to life. Usually, people represent family members in these sessions. Instead, I use colored paper squares to represent mine and, with intuition, place them on the floor where they seem to belong. I choose white for myself.

When asked to choose a color representing shame, I place a black square amid the others. As I answer questions, I sense the appropriate place and move the squares accordingly. Shame becomes visible as sexual shame due to its proximity to certain squares.

After more movement, shame, the black square, is in front of me, the white square, and we, the shame and I, appear in harmony, in balance with each other.

"You seem to be the only one in the family looking right at it. Do you see how the current positioning makes it difficult for others to see the shame? See how the mother is looking at it sideways, and the others are blocked–from seeing you–by it?" the visionary asks.

I decide to move out of the way, so the family can see me and shame separately.

In the last week of 2012, I walk along the Mississippi after a restless night. It has taken much work to find out that teaching new adults can be miserable. I'm curious about what more the PhD can do for me, and I feel too close to finishing to let it go. How much longer can I try to teach? I mentioned that to some students on the last day of that rough semester.

"You should keep teaching," one female student paused at my desk and said on her way out. What a sweet gift that was.

I learned how much damage students can cause and how difficult it is to ignore those who disturb the class so I can focus on those who want to learn.

"It is surprising how some of these inner-city recruited students getting scholarships are so nonchalant about their education," I say to someone in charge.

"Oh, they are not getting scholarships, they are getting loans," is what I hear.

This person sees my face as I imagine university representatives going into these poverty-stricken areas to sell tens of thousands of dollars of loans to young people who are already behind in schooling and the debt these students who have slim chances of graduation and high-paying jobs are accruing. I think of the immense salary of the president of the university.

"I did mention to the board in the last meeting that I thought we should stop accepting students with one-digit ACT scores," this person I am talking to says, apparently to comfort me.

In March, a friend invites my husband and me to a dinner party. A woman playwright I know from Iowa City, who inspired the outline for *Lucy, go see.*, is standing at the bar when we arrive.

"Wow," I say. "I was just thinking about you today."

"Amazing you are back in Iowa," she nods toward our friend who is preparing drinks. "I didn't know until he told me."

"It's amazing to me that I am seeing the person who inspired the genesis of the creation I am finishing," I say.

The playwright's presence feels like a gift to me from the host. I know it is a gift to himself, too, as he seats us at his sides on one end of a long oval table set for twelve under a chandelier—gold-trimmed plates shimmer around a centerpiece of sand sifting through an hourglass between flickering candelabra. "Bling," a man near the center says, waving his hand at the accoutrements. "It's all bling." And soft light. Glimmer.

The hostess is flirting with my husband at the other end of the table. The playwright's husband is in animated conversation with others near the center.

After we eat, guests play party games. Word games. Truth-telling games. I find out later about arguments and annoyances in other parts of the table, which I am unaware of at present as the host, the playwright, and I banter and laugh. At one point, the playwright looks at me with bright eyes and says, "I didn't know how funny you are."

"It's an inside joke," I say.

"Why do they disrespect me so? Without even talking to me?" I ask a friend about a group of people she knows better than I do.

"They say, 'she was a model, so she thinks she is special.' I rarely talk about you, but that night, I said I have never heard her tell even one story about modeling."

I am quiet, watching the fire.

"I wish you hadn't taken the high road," my friend says, "None of them know about his behavior. He's lying to them, and they are coddling him." She pauses. I stay quiet. "And, look, they don't even know you," she says. "I'll admit I was intimidated by how beautiful and smart you are before I met you, and then I found out how kind you are."

That is wonderful to hear.

I was invited to more parties as a married woman than I am as a single one. When the women are in charge of invitations, that is. But, also, some married men are wary, standing back as if it is wrong to talk to me now. Others make propositions. Living through this is painful, but I keep returning to the fact that I don't like most of those people, even though I try.

My sister looks tickled as she lifts the silk fabric off Mom's legs in the open casket. "She's barefoot," she says.

Mom loved being barefoot.

"How can you laugh and cry at the same time?" she asks, looking at me.

"It's funny and sad," I say, then caress Mom's calf. "Wow, this is the most alive corpse I have ever seen or felt."

"Not surprising," says our niece as she styles Mom's hair.

My sister shoos my hand as I reach to style it more the way I think Mom liked it.

"She would think it's ridiculous that we bought her a new blouse to be buried in," I say. "However, she might appreciate that we thought it inappropriate to show her cleavage."

I hate to see Mom go, and I love being there while she leaves.

On the first day of that first spring back in Iowa, the sun shines at ten degrees Fahrenheit, and the ground is covered in snow.

A Voice of the Tri-States on KDTH, my favorite local radio station, says, "Women are under more pressure than men to look young, a survey reports."

"No shit, Sherlock," I mumble as I fry three eggs from my brother's chickens.

After eating, I write. Little rainbows flash on my fingers, refracted through the crystal prisms dangling in the windows.

I pause, take a drink of coffee, and read a French philosopher claiming sperm makes man superior to woman. The coffee involuntarily spews from my mouth.

An advertisement for rape insurance comes up next on the radio.

"What on earth?" I say out loud to nobody and everybody.

On a sunny September afternoon that last fall in Dubuque, I stop at the local bakery, which, way back when, was a corner grocery where I bought candy after swimming. Now I order a cappuccino.

"Your voice is interesting; I cannot place it. Where are you from?" the cashier asks.

"Here," I say, then, "Right cheer," as Dad used to say.

The cashier's eyes widen. I like it when people are unable to place me.

A suitcase is packed, and I am ready to fly to New York City to deliver a eulogy for another mentor lost.

There is a strangeness, still, of no one at home to say goodbye to. There is also such freedom in that. No tension. Just me, about to fly again to the east in a cornflower blue sky.

Because the computer breaks down, I work on a friend's desktop. An hour or so into it, I realize I am writing about patriarchal wounds in the same room I broke down in after my grandfather's second and last instance of misconduct, the one that eventually prompted speech. Sun slants through the room like a moonbeam. I look at the orchids on the desk, then at the couch, a new one now, but in the same place where I had curled into a fetal position all those years ago.

I feel compassion for my grandfather in his wrongness and guilt for writing about it. Yet, I carry on with the work.

Later, I go to the cemetery, and, as if my voice can seep through to his bones, I tell him I am writing a rite to make things right.

Then, because I have extra time before picking up my son from hunting license practice, I visit my brother, who now owns our grandparents' house. As I park in the driveway, I stare at the garage in which a painful scene in *Lucy, go see.* takes place. The way life keeps bringing me back to the source of my work stuns me until my brother comes outside, leans in the passenger window, and says, "What's going on?"

He looks like the brother of my youth tonight, and I feel like I am in a dream while we chat in his kitchen, which I have known all my life. The sensation that I am too big for the table and the chair where I sat for so many suppers with Grandma and Grandpa is weird. Time seems to be warping inside of me. "Are you all right?" my brother asks.

I nod, then excuse myself to use the bathroom, where I remember sitting near Grandma, helping her bathe. I touch the glass doorknobs, seeing her hands there. The sink, the tub, and the toilet all seem so low to me now. I may finally be an adult.

Reality, fiction, memory, analysis: it swirls like a convergent storm, sure to eventually clear the air if I can ride it out.

I n New York City, a man offers to share his taxi from the airport, then refuses my offer to share the fare. This kindness lifts me, as does dancing on
a friend's terrace while waiting for her to come home, nine floors above the
noise and teeming humanity of Soho. Skyscrapers surround me; a full moon
rises as the setting sun reflects in the windows of the buildings opposite me. I
remember being 19 in the city, in the summer, and being intimidated, excited,
and brave.

In my mind, I'm preparing what I will say at the celebration of the life of
a dear friend I met that summer—a ballet dancer, an elder, wise and generous
and fun, gone too soon.

With another dear friend and then another, I bike around the tip of Manhattan, drink champagne and eat oysters on a sailboat, watch people dance
salsa on a pier, and enjoy my favorite dishes in a little garden at a Catalan
restaurant in Brooklyn. I look at all the faces I pass, marveling at the variety. I
can hardly stand the noise. "Is it always this loud?" I shout to the friend standing next to me as we wait to cross the street. She nods. I love Commerce
Street, Pearl Street, and the passage behind Pearl. I love being out in the world
with friends who have known my life in Europe, feeling free, and meeting new
people who love the friend we are celebrating.

It is September. Three months before I move to Chicago, though I am
unaware of that. I am aware that this is the first time I feel like me in a long
time.

C limbing Horseshoe Bluff on a narrow, worn, and ancient path high above the river, I feel wild.

In a kayak, paddling the Mississippi backwaters through a cathedral of trees, I feel free.

Leaves crinkle on trees, and their rustle has the about-to-fall quality instead of the tenacious hanging on.

Autumn is here, and the song on the wind is of loss.

alking on Chicago sidewalks in light rain. Laughing with cousins in their warm homes. Speaking French and meeting new people at a networking event for Franco-Americans. This enlivens me. As does hearing a former agent say, "The market is great now for your age group in commercials, film, and television" over breakfast the following morning, "This may be a crazy idea—but would you like to share my place for a while? You could get back into the city, I can reconnect you, and you can help me with a book I am writing on surviving sexual trauma."

"I like crazy ideas," I say. "Let me think about it."

"I think you should do it, Mom. Why wouldn't you?" my son says through the phone as I walk on Michigan Avenue.

I wonder. "I guess I am scared it might not work out."

"That's boring, Mom. Go for it. Make your new life."

"But I would have to rent a much smaller place here, and now you have the house to come home to, wouldn't you miss that?"

"Wherever you are is home, Mom."

"Chicago is only a few hours away, keep reminding yourself of that; it's not another continent. You can't *not* do this," a friend from France says through the car's sound system as I enter the Mississippi Valley. It echoes what she said four years earlier as we sat on the beach in Sitges, and I talked about the job offer in Iowa.

I am worried about leaving Mom, afraid to tell her I want to go.

I stop to see her when I get back to Dubuque. A woman who babysat me is sitting with her in the lobby. "Did you know your mom came to the hospital when I had the twins, just after my mom died? She told the nurses she was my mother, walked in, and said, 'I thought I should step in where your mom could not.'"

"That's beautiful what you did for her," I tell Mom upstairs in her apartment as we watch a Cubs game that neither of us cares about but makes us feel like Dad is in the room. I sit at her feet, massaging them, while she plays with my hair and rubs my shoulders.

"I don't know what I would do without you," she tells me.

Telling her about Chicago seems too hard at that moment.

"I keep getting the image of a watershed, and I don't even know what one is," I tell friends.

"You are a watershed. You just haven't arrived at your mouth yet," one answers.

"I felt a sort of reverse nostalgia," I say to another friend as we walk the bluffs under a beautiful moon, the smell of burning leaves in the air, a slight coolness tapping our faces.

"I am trying to figure out what reverse nostalgia is," she answers.

"Me, too. I could remember my former life there in Chicago and what was good about it, but I did not want to go back—yet I could picture myself going on there—so I guess it is a sort of nostalgia for the future?"

"You mean hope?"

Wow, I thought, *hope*. "I came to a point where I decided hope was rather useless, but I like the sound of it."

I walk for hours on the misty river that week, eyeing blue herons. Turkey vultures soar. Boats rock in slips. Trains rumble along the banks.

That weekend, I drive to Iowa City and pick up my son, and we head south to visit cousins in Missouri, where we ride horses in wheat fields as the sun sets, shoot pistols, drink tequila, dance around the fire, laugh a lot, and stand close to each other watching the full moon rise.

I ride behind him, hugging him, as he drives the four-wheeler on long stretches of gravel road under the moon.

I decide to move to Chicago.

A nephew speaks of his suspicion of women waiting to come forward with stories of sexual assault until the last three weeks of the presidential election. We are sitting on my porch. "It takes time to talk about trauma," I say, standing up. "It took me eleven years to talk about what my grandfather did."

"Don't be offended," he says, which is usually a sign of an oncoming zinger. "I would like to know how you could even go to his funeral. How could you give that eulogy you did? If I were you, I would not have even shown up."

"I am still thinking about all that," I say, deadheading marigolds and then sniffing my fingers. I love how that scent always takes me to my city grandma, Mom's mom. "I loved my grandfather and wanted to have a relationship with him. I paid a high price for wanting that, for sure."

"Grandpa, I mean *your* dad, did not know about that, right?"

"I asked Mom not to tell him, but she did."

"If anybody ever touched my child inappropriately, I would get a shotgun and walk up to them and shoot them in the head," he says.

"Remind me never to get you a shotgun," I answer as I move a gnome to a more visible spot.

My son is sad, and my husband is angry as I prepare to leave for Barcelona to defend the dissertation. Bringing them along is unaffordable in many ways. It makes me sad, too, and relieved, as tension is high at home. It is hard to be excited about one of the milestones of my life while two of the most important people in it are unhappy. I keep my joy to myself until I arrive in Catalonia.

It's July 2013; a year has passed since we left our home there. I stay at a dearly missed friend's place, where I swim and prepare my introduction. It is hard to walk around the village, no longer having a home or family in it, following in my footsteps, in a sense, through a life that has begun to seem imaginary in Iowa. "It's like it was all a dream," my son said before I left. It is good to see the beloved friends and places still there.

A week after I arrive, I pause in front of the university as if on hallowed ground, in the spot where I was most strongly hit by the mysterious orgasms twenty-five years earlier. Then I enter the building to earn a PhD with work generated and inspired by them. I think about how I initially chose Barcelona for how I feel when in it: free and connected to something I cannot name or understand.

Upstairs and outside the room where I will present my work, a supportive gathering of friends and fellows awaits me. I'm wearing one of my sister's dresses to feel my family with me. I enter and sit at a wooden table in front of an examination board of five: two male professors I know from the university, one male professor I somewhat know from Prague, and two female professors I am meeting for the first time. I like to look through the beveled windows behind the examining board. I remember the opposition from university elders, all male, about including creative work in a dissertation; one even insisted creativity did not belong in the university, saying there are other places for that. This is the first dissertation to contain creative work at the University of Barcelona, and to the best of my knowledge, on the European continent.

I open with detailed thanks to all involved, and then I mention the critical knowledge I learned from professors, scholars, and writers throughout the six years of master's and doctoral work. I look at the professor who pointed me to the mystics and beyond years ago, and I smile. "Enjoy this," he'd told me before entering the room, "you will rarely have anyone paying as much attention to your work as you do on the day of your defense."

As I open my introduction and comments, I am nervous, happy, and daring. "I had a story I wanted to tell because I thought it proved how powerful autonomy can be," I tell the board. "The story, for me, first, turned around questions about the misunderstanding between love and desire, why society considers vulnerability a weakness instead of a strength, and why there is a stigma about wounds. Why shame?"

I use my hands freely when speaking and look at each jury member often. The audience is behind me, mostly, though I can see some folks out of the corner of my eye. I detail the scholars who moved and inspired me, laying out my process map. The entire body of what I said is now mainly in the white spaces on these pages.

I say things like, "I imagine it is obvious that I believe these themes—of eros, voice, and wound—are important today and always. We must see how we wound each other. It seems vital for people to ask themselves what arouses them and to go deeply into it while considering eros an ally rather than an enemy. This seems as essential as people questioning themselves about when, how, and why they use their voices and silences. How do we use our wounds, our voice, and eros? How do we care for them in our lives? I hope this thesis opens a safe place for discussion and dialogue about these deep and private things. I hope it opens it most precisely for women as it asks them how a phallogocentric world has affected these three personal and primary aspects of their lives and autonomy."

I touch on points already written in the dissertation that these folks have already read to support what I am saying. And about an hour later, I conclude, "Both the novel and exegesis have been intense probes into the experience of being human. The overall quest of the thesis has been a quest for home. Threads and traces of domination or colonization of another's territory can be followed through antiquity, and these, too, can be called quests for home, as they are quests and (re)quests to call more and more territory home. As this exegesis illuminates Lucy Pilgrim's quest to self-construct, or in other words, to colonize herself, it suggests that human beings—descendants of colonization—unconsciously or consciously attempt colonization of the other as a way of life, wounding each other as they approach the building of lives and relationships in strategical rather than organic terms, mistakenly claiming other's territory as their own.

An individual's autonomy depends on the ability to recognize and claim oneself as one's own, and the interdependence of a community depends on the mutual respect of those personal territories. The price for this recognition can be high, and arguably, Lucy pays a high price to understand that she owns herself.

In her exploration, Lucy learns that what arouses her is life, and her connection to it, her daring to create one she wants to live and her open relationship with it. Her evolution—from a state of distrust of what is rising within her as an adolescent, which closes her and establishes a stance of defense, to an understanding of arousal as an internal compass as a young woman—opens her first to the unknown power in herself, and then, if she so chooses, to that in another.

Overall, the novel *Lucy, go see.* suggests a life of caring for self and others as a creative act, and a caring for eros, voice, and wound as the means of constructing a precious life."

"This is a light shone on patriarchy," the chair of the jury committee says after I finish.

"The novel component deserves to be published in its own right," says another jury member. Then she tilts her head a bit and looks at me, "You mention a desire to include more humor in your work, yet, I saw it throughout this novel, and," she raises a finger, "I also appreciated the soundtrack."

"One can trace the relationship of support moving from father to mother as the young woman grows," another committee member says.

"Your doctorate is conferred with mention of excellence," the chair says in closing.

"You are the bravest woman I know," an audience member says as she presents me with a gift and congratulations.

Seven years of focus are finished.

I glide on marble floors through slants of sunlight amid colonnades, knowing I have done what I set out to do. After a celebratory lunch with the committee and advisors, I stroll favorite streets of Barcelona. Later, I attend a small and delicious garden dinner in my honor in the hills.

"What have you been doing all day?" Mom asks when I come to see her. It's November 2016.

"Writing, reading, job applying, paperwork, exercise, taking things off walls," I say.

"Why were you taking things off walls?"

"I want to talk to you about that."

"You're moving away, aren't you?" she says.

I nod, then watch her swallow the information in a way that reminds me of how my son took the news of his parents' divorce.

After a moment, she turns and looks into my eyes. "How can I help?" is what she says.

Oh, how I love my mom.

"Are you going back over to Spain?" my godmother asks. We are at her place for supper.

"No, just Chicago," I say.

Mom shakes the ice in her rum and coke and says, "I may live with her downtown there."

"You're gonna love it, but where are you going to park?" my godmother asks me.

"That's the least of my worries. Where am I going to work?"

She nods, then says, "I have a friend whose sister worked at a jewelry store there in the tower with that jerk's name on it," my godmother says. "She said that he came in one day and slid his hand along her leg, and she lifted a fork and said, 'Get your hands off me, or I am going to put this fork through your nuts.' He went upstairs to the boss and tried to get her fired, but he refused to fire her."

We're all worried about what might happen to our country if this man becomes president.

"How are you feeling about it all?" a friend asks.

"Disappointed and sad," I say.

"I love how you talk about it and don't talk about it," he says.

"I'm shocked when people tell me not to be sad, that it isn't sad, that they aren't sad about leaving their husbands," I say to a former classmate as we sit alone at a picnic table during a high school reunion.

"I know," she says, "I always want to answer *did you love him?*"

"I imagine that a lot of your sadness has to do with the fact that he denies your sorrow," another friend says while sitting on the back porch with me, candles flickering.

I nod. *Desecration* is a word that comes to mind.

One of Mom's dear friends, the woman who took me to breakfast and helped get Dad into the nursing home, dies. She was also a friend to me, a staunch supporter of my PhD, always asking about it, cheering me on, and expressing her admiration.

I hate to see her go, too.

Mom and I stand in the sun and wind on long green grass, next to corn fields, near the gaping grave, looking over the far horizon. Her friends, many of them mutual friends of my parents—mainly the women are left—lean on walkers or canes or hold onto a loved one's arm. A man I have known all my life sings a hymn in a beautiful baritone alongside the casket, and then it is lowered.

After we toss flowers, pray, hug friends, and express our sympathy again to her family, I take Mom for a drive.

"How are things going with your book?" she asks. She knows what is in it.

"I'm thinking I will use a pseudonym," I say.

"That would be a good thing." It sounds like she is talking about getting an ice cream cone which we both like to do. "What's the title?" she asks.

"Lucy, go see?"

"I like that," she answers, repeating the words while keeping her eyes on the road.

After the librarian introduces me to a workshop audience I lead, which the alchemist tells me afterward is the most alchemical workshop she has ever seen, surprising me, a woman who has known me since I was 12 writes to say, "I had no idea how much you have done. You are much too modest."

What am I supposed to do? I'm thinking. Go around telling people everything I've done? I wonder who can stand that.

Right now, writing this seems immodest. Yet, it's part of the story of how I came to know myself better, how I came home.

Alchemy. I love the sound of the word. The process. What it all boils down to. 432,000 words morph into 48,000—that kind of transformation.

I walk around a neighborhood the Democratic Party assigned to me, knocking on doors to see if anyone needs help to vote.

"I would like to see a *mom* in the White House, to have a *mom* in charge," one voter tells me.

At the nearby cemetery, where Mom's mom, my city grandma, is buried, I place an *I'm with her* sticker on her grave.

On Election Day, I prepare a list of furnishings to sell, then head to Mom's to watch returns. I serve us each a rum and Coke with a bowl of Cheetos. This might have clued me in.

I remember Mom hugging me and saying, "That could be us," while watching the first female presidential nominee and her daughter on stage at the Democratic convention in July. I remember her calling me upset after watching the Republican convention and how I reassured her our country would never put that man in such a position of power, and she was relieved.

It's horrible watching the returns come in. In the wee hours of the morning, a friend in France texts, *Turn off the TV. Go to bed.*

I toss and turn, leave the pull-out bed and lie beside Mom. Still unable to sleep, unable to believe that millions are okay with this person representing our country, I search my brain, imagining where his supporters are in my hometown. At least those houses with signs on the lawns are easily identifiable. I see the faces of those in my family who are happy about this and am especially confused by their proclaimed Christianity alongside this choice.

When day breaks, I look at my phone filled with messages from distraught friends, giving and seeking consolation. I shower, dress, walk downstairs to the almost-empty dining room and fill two cups of coffee. A rusted tin taste permeates the air as if acid or some other toxic substance was thrown all over the place during the night. I think of the young nurse who gave Mom eyedrops the night before and how worried she was about this outcome.

Mom and I drink the coffee upstairs. "What if we turn the television on?" she says.

"She will speak in a half-hour; you watch if you want. I can't bear it," I say.

"Well, honey, there is still time. She did get more votes. You never know what might happen next."

Thinking how excited Mom was to see a woman president in her lifetime recalls when she talked to me about her three daughters and how we were out in the world and doing things on our own. "I couldn't, but you girls can," she said in haunting acceptance.

"If she were a man, she would have been elected; she would have been forgiven her shortcomings," I say that afternoon, then go for a walk in the woods, listening to the gurgling of the creek, enjoying the sun and wind on my skin, watching squirrels rustle in the drying leaves. I lie down on a bench and text my son, who voted for her though she wasn't his first choice. He calls. "This is a sad day for America, Mom," he says.

He tells me about fraternity brothers whooping and celebrating in other rooms of the house. I ask him to believe we will rise to deal with this outcome. After our chat, he leaves his room for the first time that day.

The long way home passes by my godmother's. She is outside, checking her mail. I pull into the driveway. "Isn't this just the shits?" she says.

Once home, I call a cousin, and we meet and walk the city streets in the dark. Eventually, we stop at a pizzeria and eat, drink wine, and finally, laugh enough to face the world again.

"There are claw marks on the walls here," a friend says after she calls from New York City, and I ask how she is.

It is raining and misty the morning a student, an Iraqi war vet, breaks down in French class because he is unable to remember what he is learning.

I tell him it's okay, I go over it with him again, and I point out where he is doing well, yet it is impossible to console him. Tears run down his cheeks as he says, "I can't, I can't, I see the words, and then they don't fit inside my head, they all fall into letters, and nothing makes sense, and I can't put them together, and well, I can't do anything right. It's awful. I'm losing everything."

"I keep looking at the door, thinking Dad might walk in," I say at a family Christmas party.

"Oh, he's here," my sister says, twirling her finger in the air.

Mom is playing dominoes, surrounded by grandkids. It is her turn, and she is taking her time.

"Grandma, this is not all about you," one of her grandsons says.

"Oh, yes, it is," Mom says, carefully placing a domino. "In some way, a big way, it is."

I chuckle, then step outside for some air. My son is on my niece's swing, gently rocking. "Wanna go for a walk, Mom?"

We walk up the hill, our steps cracking through the ice. We toss pieces of it around like Frisbees to watch them shatter where they hit. "Mom, I think in English now," he tells me.

"That's good, right?" I ask.

"It's great; it's less confusing. For a long time, I translated from Spanish and French to English in my head before speaking, and now I don't have to." He lifts me then and carries me for a while. The light of a tractor probes a snowy field, the sky softly darkens, and twilight sparkles in the trees covered in ice.

"Are you writing all this down? Are you getting all this in there? This is so damn rich. I think you should make this a memoir. All this stuff you are telling me with being here, leaving, your grandfather, all these things coming back around," a friend says as we sit in front of the fire at my home.

"I am writing," I say.

"I see a rent sign in the front yard?"

I nod. "I'm moving. To Chicago. At the end of the year."

"It's so damn unfair," my friend says, shaking his head.

I love all the fires I build and sit in front of, alone, with my son, or with friends. These warm and intimate fireside chats are my social life, my private salon. I sit with another friend in front of another fire, another day at home.

"Here's to my move!" I say, lifting a glass of cava.

"I can't cheer to that," says this friend who told me what a surprise I was, how she never imagined having a friend like me. Her voice is small and low in a way I have never heard. "You know I am happy for you, though, and I think this is the absolute next move for you."

I do know, and I also feel sad and think it is unfair. Life is like that sometimes.

"That is so pretty, what a pretty tree," Mom repeats on Christmas Eve. I'm thrilled to have her in our home for Christmas, for once. All those years abroad, it was hard to be far from family at this time of year, even if the holidays were more manageable and warmer in Sitges. If we had to choose one trip a year, it was usually for a month in the summer.

"I always loved how you hung thin strands of tinsel on the branches when we were little, so I did it, too," I tell Mom.

"You did a beautiful job, honey," she says.

This is her third Christmas without Dad, our first in the apartment on Main Street, and though we are unaware, our last as a family.

Mom seems happy, and that makes me happy.

We eat cheese fondue and later lychees, clementines, and chocolates. Christmas music accompanies the fire surreally burning on the television screen. It's almost like our Christmases by the sea.

Mom stays overnight; that's another first, which makes me happy for my son, too, to have his grandma in his home. In the morning, we drink coffee and eat croissants, then open presents of perfumes and sweaters and scarves. It's lovely thanking, kissing, hugging, and sniffing each other. Our son has a part-time job now, and he has given us generous and thoughtful gifts, and he is as proud of that as we are of him.

Later, Mom leaves with one of my brothers, then the three of us head to the Mines of Spain, a state park. We crunch through snowy trails to the frozen Mississippi and walk along its banks. Giant snowflakes drop like confetti. We pussyfoot onto the iced river, marveling at our ability to stand out on the channel. "My cousin said my uncle used to drive his truck out here and do doughnuts," I say. The snow piles higher and higher as we spin, laughing in delight and disbelief. It's as if we are in a magical and mystical dream. Sky, ground, trees, bridge, river, bluffs, us—everything is white.

When asked, by e-mail, why I left, I attempt a succinct answer.
I was no longer able to maintain a relationship that was not growing.
I look at the line of words, that *no* and that *not* clunk.
I consider ways to remove the *not* as I often tell my students to do.
"Take out the *not*s," I say. "Un-*not* your work as much as possible."
For instance—I refuse to stay in a stagnant relationship.

European starlings gather on the chimney of the funeral home. It is almost spring. I am teaching an Advanced Writing class at a new university, and I have students who love me. I love the drive to work across the river, passing through a threshold of limestone outcroppings salted with snow. Over the following weeks, I watch mounds of ice melt from the stones, then flow, then trees sprout from crevices.

I volunteer as a timer at my son's swim meet. At the edge of the pool, splashed by glistening teenaged-boy bodies, watching my son make his way amid them, I try to remember loving boys that age, being that age.

"Live with me; stay here," Mom repeats.

"Are you saying you want me to move in with you and hang out with you all the time?"

"Yes."

"Jesus, Mom."

A friend calls from Paris, and our conversation makes me feel like my younger self, the one in the picture I came across on a twenty-year-old Parisian public transport pass that morning. I stir burning postcards and letters, watching the penmanship, stamps, and images go up in flame and dissolve into ash as we talk about the upcoming move to Chicago. "I'm purging again," I say, "I love burning the meaningless, unnecessary, and cumbersome."

"Up in smoke and out the chimney it goes," she adds.

"I'm watching out the window, waiting for a friend who will help me take some things to my boy," I say, then put my hand in my pants pocket and find a twenty-dollar bill. It's a good morning, all in all.

My friend is my friend's husband and feels like a favorite brother-in-law to me. He pulls his pickup into the driveway, and we load my son's bed onto it. On our way to Iowa City, this good man points to the cold, rolling fields. "Now that they do not drop any seed with their new threshing systems, these are like deserts–no birds out here. No deer. No animal life."

We are quiet for a while, thinking about what this means.

Until I say, "I appreciate your help. I wish my son's father were doing this for him."

"Leave that man here when you go to Chicago, please," he says, without taking his eyes from the road. "I already think you are wonderful to be around, but you must be even more fun when you don't have that twisted little French fucker bothering your life."

"The therapist told me he has a part of me, and I need to get it back," I say. "I keep wondering what part she means."

"I'd like to know what part he doesn't have," my friend says. "And I say that with all my love."

That is hard and good to hear.

In Iowa City, when I start to help my friend take the mattress off the truck, he gently places his hand on my forearm to stop me, nods toward my son, and says, "Let him do it."

It is hard to know how much is too much. I feel like I have to be a mother and father to pick up the slack. I even want to, thinking it will help my son and me feel less lack, but it doesn't. A mom is a mom; a dad is a dad–no way to be both.

The next day, I enjoy lunch with another male friend at a tiny clapboard restaurant on a county backroad out in the middle of waves of snow. He flirts with me.

"Listen, sir," I say, "if you are ever a single person, we'll talk."

He raises an eyebrow and keeps it raised. "Talk?" he says.

The last days in Dubuque are as rich as the first but much harder.

Five days before I have to be out of the house, exhausted and at the task, I hear the front door open and look down the stairs. An aunt is stomping the snow off her boots. She looks up at me. I see my grandmother, grandfather, and father in her face.

"I'm leaving if you're gonna cry," she says.

We spend hours making piles to keep or take to Goodwill while discussing family dilemmas. Many boxes of what I want to keep are already in friends' closets. My aunt stops me from tossing some things. "I've got the room; I'm keeping that stuff for you." She makes some phone calls and then tells me her sons will come the next day to remove a gigantic television too heavy for me to lift.

I keep packing. "My god, girl, you have enough dishes to feed an army. By the way, when was the last time you ate something?"

"I can't remember."

"I'm going to A&W and get you a cheeseburger and fries. You want a root beer?"

"I'd love one."

That night, after we load everything into her SUV, I ask, "Will you also take care of the little fox for me?" handing her the bobblehead planter.

We drop off piles of stuff at Goodwill, and then she drives us to a local ski resort to listen to live music. My sister is there. My aunt buys me an Old Fashioned, orders me another meal, looks at my sister, nods toward me, and says, "Get her another drink."

My sister's support of the person soon to occupy the Oval Office mysti-fies me. The distance I feel from her pains me, and I imagine she is as sad that I am leaving as she had been happy when I arrived. She'd taken it stoically when I told her in my kitchen a month earlier, but we hadn't seen each other much since then. "I don't know what I would do without you here," she said once, her voice cracking into tears over the phone.

The last afternoon of the year, still packing and sorting, I take a break and invite Mom to do errands with me. "I will miss seeing all this," she says, wav-ing her hand at the signs, stores, and restaurants on Kennedy Road.

"Miss this? This is the worst, most boring street in Dubuque."

"Who is going to take me anywhere anymore?"

"Your baby daughter takes you lots of places; your sons are here. Your other daughter is ninety miles away."

"Mmhmm," she says, nodding.

When we return, the New Year's Eve party at her residence is at full tilt. It is a relief to say goodbye to her amid festivity, walking her into a party. "See you soon," I say as we hug, then she moves into the crowd of friends opening their arms to greet her.

I back away, watching, until she is out of my sight. It's wrenching to go.

Back at the house, I text hosts of parties I was invited to and say I won't make it.

As I pack, a friend texts me a link to Steve Miller's "Fly Like An Eagle," and I put it on repeat, playing it all night long.

The plan was to sleep at my friends' place that night, but it is three in the morning when I run out of steam, curl up on the carpeted floor, and sleep near the same spot I sat with those friends the day I moved in.

Backing out of the driveway, I brake and see again my mom and son waving from the glider on the porch the summer before. The friends and family who graced my home. The birthday and graduation parties for my son. Mom's 88th birthday party, when I made a cake and realized MOM is WOW upside down.

A ceramic owl, the only tangible thing left behind, other than perennials I planted, smiles at me as if to say *you know you'll be fine.*

I've finally come to accept I'll feel trammeled and besieged as long as the man I left is in town, though I wish it otherwise.

I need time in a clearer field.

Some think he stays to torture me. Others ask where else he has to go. I can think of many places. Some consider my hometown a perfect place for him to hide and make up stories about his life to tell faraway friends. One thinks stealing my life is his aim.

But beyond all this, I feel life itself nudging me back into the world.

I'll still be close enough to Mom and my son.

I am the first to arrive and toast the new year with friends who did so much for me without my asking, who made me laugh, and who sat quietly nearby while I cried.

I whisper goodbye, then slip out the back door as the party grows.

From Chicago, in those first weeks living with my former agent in her twenty-first-floor condo on Ohio Street, I call Mom.

"I am just sitting at the window watching cars coming and going. I wish I could get around by myself," she says.

"I bet you do. You must miss driving so much. I'm watching cars, too, from a slightly higher perspective than yours, but anyway, we're doing the same thing, Mom," I say, thinking old age will be an excellent time to live in a pedestrian village near the sea.

During those first weeks, I get myself in shape by working out in the building's fancy gym in the mornings, walking all over the city in the late afternoons, and practicing yoga in a studio downtown at night. I edit for my rent, write for me, apply for jobs, visit the Newberry, join the Art Institute and the Alliance Française, attend film festivals and get to know people who introduce me to more people and exciting events. When I feel ready, I have new headshots taken, sign with an agency, and hang out at my old haunt, the 3rd Coast Café. On Valentine's Day, I sign a lease on a studio in that building. I practice and audition for voice-overs, commercials, and films, and eventually take a job at a fancy soap shop, Sabon, to have some steady income. I visit Mom twice a month, sometimes more.

In the late summer, I meet a businessman who eventually becomes a lover. The morning after a tender evening entwined, laughing before sleep, in the wee hours, and upon waking, I swim, dip, and stand in the lake, letting its refreshing coolness enter my bones. I'm excited because I thought I might never feel this way again. After he raises his hand above his head to tell me, "I want you to always consider yourself above me," I shake my head and tell him we are on the same level. In the end, it seems he desired to lift me so he could have fun knocking me down, a sort of domination fantasy. But, for a while, we have fun, and he seems reasonable and sweet and kind and generous until he doesn't. It's so disappointing that I prefer to keep it brief.

But this is insignificant and, in fact, a distraction; it's lovely for a while, but still a distraction. Once I turn away from it, I finish and publish *Lucy, go see*. That Thanksgiving, my son wants to celebrate this and asks if the novel has a theme song. I tell him one that could be. He finds it on his phone, slips his speaker from the inside pocket of his jacket, and we dance to it on the bridge over the Iowa River under the stars on a chilly night.

Three months before I separate, at the edge of a long, hard winter, I fly to Seattle to convene with ten thousand other writers and meet privately with a few award-winners I have long admired and would like to invite to Dubuque. At a historic hotel, the MarQueen, an aversion to calling home puzzles me. Later, it will seem as if the body was preparing to go before the mind could grasp it.

Walking helps thinking, so I look around Queen Anne and see a Russian bathhouse that reminds me of Japanese bathhouses I love. They offer an excellent deal for a three-day pass, so I buy one and enjoy all the physical and spiritual benefits of water nightly. It restores me.

Morning breakfasts in the art deco lounge. Walks along the shoreline to the convention center. Reading poetry I translated in a club with red lights on a purple stage. Listening to my former housemate read her poetry in a packed art gallery. I cross paths with writers I have met in other places and countries. I meet privately with American writers who inspire and move me, and I am thrilled to look into their eyes and tell them about my plan to set up a writing event in Dubuque and ask if they would come and what they would need to make that happen.

It rains. The sun shines. Giant red hibiscus bloom. Morning glories spiral a pole. Sometimes I feel like I am in Japan, or Hong Kong, on the other side of the Pacific again.

On the last day, I ride a ferry to Bainbridge Island, then wander.

In a stationery store, a young woman tells me, "Right now, I'm working here, studying, modeling, and wanting to travel."

"You will," I say, "you'll see."

"You were the most successful person there—do you realize that? You hit four out of four," the alchemist says in Madison, where we are attending a pitch-fest in April.

"This novel pitching reminds me of modeling or commercial auditions," I say.

"Does that make it easier to face the possible rejection?" she asks.

"It was easier in modeling because it was about how I looked. This is about my soul. I guess I am going from selling my looks to selling my soul, though I've always thought my soul could be seen in my looks." I sigh. "At least literary agents don't ask how much I weigh or tell me to turn around for a fuller view of my backside."

hat I want that last spring–before I make a life-altering decision–is travel.

Instead, I drive to the river and sit at a picnic table, envying a pelican, crane, and gull floating south on driftwood. Then I go to my office.

A departing colleague wonders if I, or perhaps my husband, would like to lead the French program for a year starting the following fall. I am faced with helping my husband or myself.

"Let him get his own job," Mom says.

I prepare a class for the interview and am offered the job.

I keep that to myself. It's hard. It's all so hard.

I miss a part of me but saying exactly which eludes me, and I believe river, tree, bird, and sky will eventually tell me. So, after the semester ends, I drive county roads out in the middle of what seems like nowhere.

Independence–a mythic place in my imagination because it's the hunting grounds of the men of my family– is surprisingly abandoned and rundown. As I stroll, looking at murals and for signs of life, I notice a neon sign–The Sanity Room. I laugh when I see it is closed. On the bridge over the Wapsipinicon River, I pause to feel the dam's power and the coolness of the mist. Then, I drive on.

In Spillville, a two-story brick building that reminds me of a French country house has a sign for a clock museum on it. I park. Two women greet me, and one leads me to wonders created by bachelor brothers who never traveled beyond a hundred-mile radius of the family farm. They spent their early-twentieth-century lives reading, carving, and building ornate clocks, some nine feet tall–all telling animated stories of a world they gleaned from books. Above the clock-filled room, I wander through rooms filled with stories of the summer Antonin Dvorak worked and lived there with his family.

In Elkader, which may be the only town in America named for an Islamic hero, I eat couscous on a stone terrace with a view of an arched limestone bridge over the Turkey River and feel like I'm in Europe.

At Iowa's Pike's Peak, the highest bluff above the confluence of the Mississippi and Wisconsin rivers, I imagine French explorers canoeing amid the green crowns of treetops over three hundred springtimes ago.

A breeding male Indigo Bunting flits amid lilacs next to me.

Text messages tumble in now that I have reentered covered territory. One tells me I have been awarded an honorable mention for a flash fiction piece and that a chapter of *Lucy, go see.* has been accepted for publication. "Where are you, and when are you coming back?" Mom asks via voice mail.

I park at a hotel on the river in Marquette and book a room, then walk to a casino on a riverboat anchored at the shore, buy a hot dog and beer, then carry these delicacies outside to the back deck, and sit next to the train tracks eating, thinking of Dad, who loved hot dogs, and imagining life in a houseboat. My legs dangle high above the water, and I feel like Humpty Dumpty. I no longer wonder what I am going to do. I am doing it.

The following day I stay in bed until five minutes before checking out, looking at maps, river, passing trains, changing skies. I will do this often in the next decade; I've only just begun. I watch a man steer his fishing boat into a deeper channel. Harleys rev in the parking lot.

Are there lovers who never hurt each other? I wonder. Is this possible? I wish. I want to be one.

I drive.

The relief I feel at the sight of my mother surprises me.

I n late June, in the blue room–a room at a friend's place where I write each day after swimming–the visionary asks, via Skype, "So what do you want to work on today?"

"I want to unravel the knot I feel myself in."

"Close your eyes, and tell me where you feel it."

"It seems to be in the gut, but difficult to pinpoint."

"Just stay quiet; feel for it." She waits. "Where do you feel it now?"

"The uterus."

My eyes closed, and on my back, I feel something like contractions and see wilting white peonies floating out of me. My husband appears in this vision–sitting at my side, his hand cupping my knee as it was when I gave birth to our son. "It seems I am giving birth to peonies, which are tinged and rusty around the edges. I sense they have lived, blossomed, and flourished and are now being excused. A great lightness comes over me as they leave. This is wild."

My breaths deepen, and my legs relax to the sides.

"What do you feel now?"

"I feel like an upside-down turtle with no protection. I feel completely exposed."

"You are," she says.

The released peonies rise like balloons and float away. Veil-like layers of protection follow suit, lifting and flying away. Unstoppable laughter punctuates my speech as I say, "I see turtles flying. Pink turtles."

When the wonderful laughter tapers off, I say what I see. "Expelling the peonies brought an immense surge of freedom. The turtles and peonies are parting ways now, and the turtles are flying toward mountains. I feel excitement rising between my legs."

"So, do you feel any knots now?"

"Nope," I pause, feeling the calm inside. "God, I love my body," I say for the first time in my life.

"I'm in deep trouble," Mom calls to say. "I can't find the bank book, and I am about out of my mind wondering who has their hands on it around here."

I drive to her place, lift furniture, look in drawers, and find it under the recliner. "How did you do that?" she says, almost mad at me. "I looked everywhere."

"Magic, Mom."

"Oh, honey, thank you, I am sorry I bothered you. What were you doing?"

"My June routine: I get up at dawn, put on my bathing suit—you know, like when I was little at the cottage—then I climb through the window to sit on the roof, where I drink coffee and watch birds, then I put on shorts and sandals and drive to Municipal pool, park, walk along the river, drop shorts and sandals at pool's edge, then dive in and swim laps. I watch eagles, clouds, and turkey vultures while I backstroke. I love watching and listening to the passing trains. Then I go home for lunch, then I write."

"What?" Mom says.

"I am working on a short story that begins at an academic conference on eros in Ontario, Canada, and ends with a Christlike figure at Chalice Wells in Glastonbury, England."

"Oh. What do you do after that?"

"I edit home movies and read. Sometimes I sit out on the roof at sunset. I came across a short movie of Dad out back on the swing that I could show you—it's great to see and hear him again. Also, I'll take you if you want to go to the pool with me. We could do some walking in the water."

"Maybe one day. What's your husband doing?"

"I'm tired of asking."

"What about your son?"

"He's working at the arboretum. He likes it."

Rain falls. It pours hard all night, and flash floods cover the riverfront.

At home, I gather the unopened peony buds from a friend's gift bouquet and stand them in a glass on the windowsill. They look like Tootsie Pops, their buds softening without opening.

Mom calls again, "Turn on the television and watch *America's Got Talent*. You will like it. Just turn it on and call me later."

That same month, June 2014, I come upon what appears to be hidden money while putting clean socks in a drawer. This is the second time I have found a money stash; a friend will remind me.

Alone at home, I pace the apartment knowing all other ways to look are gone. I wait to say something, checking back occasionally and noticing the quantity decreases.

One afternoon, I ask how long total support is expected of me, and when I hear it is as long as I am able, I say I am no longer able. The French sentence *Je ne peux plus te supporter* comes to mind. It looks like *I can no longer support you,* but it means *I can no longer stand you.* I guess they are the same thing, in a way.

When I ask about the hidden money, I witness what looks like dramatic surprise, then receive thanks for discovering the forgotten wealth. When I mention the diminishing quantity, I receive fury and accusations of intentional invasion of privacy.

Knowing the person I may leave has subsistence brings peace of mind.

While swimming–and after a long time of estimating the possible personal and collateral damages of staying or going–a bolt of surety enters my system like a piston.

" I will tell the landlord we are moving in August unless you want to keep the apartment. I am going to look for another place to live. Unless you are willing to work on our relationship, yourself, or get a job, I am finished living like this," I say.

I feel stronger now than the woman I was a week or so earlier, begging him to leave, blubbering, "Please don't make me leave you in my hometown. All you do is tell me how unhappy you are here and how ignorant everyone is. Please go."

The person to whom I have given everything I can for twenty-six years asks me if I love him.

"This has little to do with love. This is about your behavior," I answer, pricking myself by accident with the mending needle between my fingers.

An insult flies my way.

I lick the blood from my finger, look up, and say, "That's part of the behavior I am talking about."

I see and hear the words "I know," whispered, then watch the long-cherished man spring off the couch like a swift and dart out of the room.

This declaration of knowledge I keep in my heart.

It helps.

I learn that making no choice is a choice.

Over the Fourth of July weekend, my son and I go to Chicago and enjoy cousins and the city, then join the immediate family and lifelong family friends for a reunion. Picnics, barbecues, baseball, four-wheeling, volleyball, fireworks, fires, swimming, stories, and laughter. I love watching my son have fun. I hate thinking about what I have to tell him.

"What is going on with your husband?" a brother asks when we are alone.

"I invited him. He declined my offer. A few days ago, I told him that unless things changed, I would move out by August 1. I'm looking for a place big enough for all of us in case things improve."

"He never did want to work, you know," my brother says. I don't know what to say. It seems more complex than that. My brother looks at my son, who is walking our way, "Does he know?"

"No. I wanted both of us to tell him, but his father says he can't. I was going to tell him on the drive here, but it never seemed the right moment."

"Let him have this weekend. Tell him on the way back," my brother says.

God, I hate having to do that.

I tell him on a bench at one of my favorite places. The river, far below, looks like a silver-plated mirror. A slight, warm wind lifts the leaves; the grass is long and lush. "I love the way rivers keep moving," I say, gathering my courage. Then I tell my son what I told my brother.

The sight of burgeoning sycamores and the river's bend soothes me as I witness the shock, anguish, relief, and heartbreak passing through my grown child. I want to touch him, but it seems best to give him space, so I sit quietly next to him until he says, "Let's go."

On the way home, he says something I can't repeat, which tells me he understands my choice, which is a gift.

We are alone at home when we arrive. When I come out of the bathroom, I see my son sitting on the roof, looking at the bluffs, and wiping away tears. I want to airlift us far away.

It takes a few weeks of searching to find a new home. I hate how going around town on my own to ask about places to rent makes me look so obviously on the verge of separation, even though I am. Only my immediate family and a friend in New York City know what's going on. As the search continues, I deal with more difficult behaviors at home. One particularly awful night, from my sleeping place for months now, an air mattress under an open window, I look up and beg Dad to help me find a good, safe home for my son and me.

I check Craig's List at dawn and see a new rental on the screen. I immediately write and ask to see it. I am the first person I will learn later, which is why I will get it. Then, I go for a walk and swim. While I am watching turtles along the river, the homeowner calls. "I know you," he says when I tell him my name. "We went to high school together."

I drive to see the house after I swim. As soon as I follow the owner inside, I feel this is it, a feeling amplified with each new view–of the kitchen, back patio, flower garden, basketball court, fireplace, hardwood floors, front porch, spacious roomy upstairs, and passersby on the sidewalk in front. It costs more than the apartment, but I will make more at the university that fall. I call within hours to say I'd like it. The time I wait for confirmation is nerve-wracking. I worry needlessly about credit rating, whether the landlord might have figured out I am separating, whether his wife will want a single woman next door, and whether they will believe I can afford it on my own. This is the year 2014, a friend reminds me when I worry aloud.

I also want to know if I should keep looking for other places because August will soon be here. I do all this worrying on the first morning when thankfully, the phone rings. "I would like to introduce to you a Spanish filmmaker who is in town. Will you have lunch with us?" the director of the local film festival asks.

Eyes widen around the table as I speak Spanish with the Spaniard, who appears amazed that this is happening in Dubuque. "Do you know this woman has worked with three of Spain's best directors?" he asks the table of six.

"You have to come out on the river with us," the director says.

"I need to look for an apartment," I say, "I think I found one, but I'm waiting for confirmation."

"It's Friday at 3 pm. I think the apartment search can wait. A trip on the Mississippi is what you need," he says, and I agree.

While I sit back and sip a glass of wine, the wind whips the worry out of my head, the sun covers me in kisses, and a text beeps on my phone, confirming the new home will be mine as soon as the credit and background checks come back clean.

Soon after, a $1,000 check arrives in the mail, because of an error in former tax returns, just in time for the deposit.

I feel lucky again.

I count the days, less than two weeks, before moving out. There is no time for sadness; so much has to be done— including the five-day contemplative retreat I booked at a nearby monastery for the last week of July.

The afternoon I settle into a little stone house in the valley that I will have to myself for the duration, the jangle of the rotary wall telephone startles me. One of the Trappistine sisters asks, "Do you have everything you need?"

"I do."

"We will stop in with fresh vegetables. We have vigils, lauds, vespers, and mass daily, and you are welcome to join us. If you need anything, say so; otherwise, we will leave you in peace," she tells me. Using a rotary dial wall phone makes me feel like a girl again.

"Our Lady of the Mississippi Abbey," I say to myself, smiling, as I make tea. Then I wander up and down stairs. The sun illuminates the rooms of the house. The window views are of fields, valleys, tree lines, or sky. Looking out, I catch a glimpse of a woman standing over the seat of a green tractor, her long brown hair flying, a smile on her face as she heads up the winding gravel road toward the main house.

I pick up a book and read about healthy groups of people living in a deliberately chosen spirit of risk, adventure, courage, and openness, in what the writer calls a spirit of insecurity, embracing an unknown future in an attitude of honest questioning.

I look for my notebook to write that down before I head outside. I meet Richard Rohr there through his work.

After walking amid the cornfields and cows, I sit by a brook. My body opens and lengthens—laughter and delight rise in my chest. It's strange to notice how sometimes I feel the weight of things more clearly when they are gone.

Fresh beans, eggs, garlic, and bread are on the kitchen table when I return. I light a fire in the grill. As the sky darkens, I watch the sunset from the picnic table where I eat, imagining ancestors from places like Prussia, Southern England, and Liechtenstein arriving at this valley more than a century ago. I wonder what they carried in their hearts and on their person, how long it took to get here, and what paths they traveled. Lightning bugs emit constellations above the grass and fields. I shake my head at my unconscious cruelty as a girl, pulling off their glowing bellies–mating radars–and wearing them as jewelry. Stars fall. I stay outside longer, listening to the animals moving around in the dark.

The first morning, I walk up the gravel road to the chapel and sit Vigil. I love the quiet inside, the coolness and shadows, and the organ music. Afterward, one sister tells me she put my name in the prayer box, and two hundred people are praying for me.

Another sister, who looks like the woman I have seen on the tractor, approaches as I leave Vespers. She asks to speak to me outside and leans toward me, "Do you have enough food?"

"I think I do."

"Follow me," she says, then takes me around the chapel to a back door. "Wait here," she says, then enters, and when she returns, she hands me a bag filled with grapes, broccoli, and butter beans. "Have you been to the pond?"

"There's a pond?"

"Just follow the path through the corn; you will see a cabin there; it is the only building older than the stone house."

The pond is the shape of a colossal kidney bean, reflecting the tall grasses surrounding it and the agate sky. Blue dragonflies flit in squadrons above it. I sit on the dock watching them until I am hungry.

During those meals outside at dusk, I tell myself I will have to get used to being a single parent. You often felt like one anyway, my self answers. The loss of an illusion, a dream, is worse than the loss of reality. What people might say and think, that flimsy concern flits around me, too. Most folks see what we think we are hiding, anyway. Losing face is the hardest and losing face with oneself is the worst. A wind picks up. Coyotes cry. A deer snorts and then runs. Before I turn in, I set the alarm for 3:15.

Walking up the hill in the darkest dark, wondering if I have ever seen so many stars, I inhale the scent of the sixty-foot pines lining the curvy ascending path. A sliver of light shines on the moon, and oak leaves rustle in the wind.

Inside the chapel, I sit in a pew facing the sisters, their heads bowed, reading bibles. A faint light illuminates an open book on the pulpit, and a sister reads aloud. I think about the timeless power of writing and reading.

Another morning after Lauds, a sister approaches me as I reach for the door handle in the vestibule. Her eyes remind me of my grandmother's, my father's mother's. "Is there anything you need, dear?" she asks.

I pause, looking for words. "I keep wondering if I am asking myself the right questions," I say.

She tilts her head as if to let that need drop more profoundly into the ear she heard it from. "If it were me, I would say the best questions to ask myself are 'What is my relationship with God, and what can I do to strengthen that?'"

Sulphur butterflies flit from one side of the path to the other as if consecrating the ground before me as I walk back to the house, thinking about God, a mystery I am reluctant to name. A force greater than me, this I know exists, but as soon as I put a name or body on it, I'm lost. I think of a swami who wrote *GOD*, an acronym for *GO Deep*. I like this.

Everyone I read and listen to at the abbey points to this question of one's relationship with God, with the divine. Relationship, relationship, relationship—the word turns in my mind.

The beauty of my questioning is realizing—for as long as I can remember—I have made *relationships* God instead of having a relationship *with* God. As if relationships with other people are more important than my connection with the divine.

This insight changes my life.

The last evening at the abbey, a brother calls to tell me that Mom is in the hospital, and she is okay, and he is with her, so I stay for the intended duration until the following day.

When I arrive at Mom's side, I learn she fell in the night and spent hours on the floor, struggling to find a way to her feet or the phone, screaming for help. Her voice is hoarse, and her throat is sore. I stay at her side through the night.

In the morning, she asks for news. I tell her the reasons why and when I am moving out. "Oh, honey," she says, squeezing my hand at the painful parts.

Once home, I watch a hand wave, as if over a vast domain, and hear "take it all."

"Everything?" I ask.

I am instructed to leave papers and clothes.

So I do. It's a big job, and weird to do it alone in a home of three. I make meals for the family until the end to obtain some sense of normalcy. This is also weird. I am copying Emmanuelle Béart, who I once saw tell a lover she was leaving as she placed a meal in front of him. She then picked up her suitcase and left. This nobleness of offering nourishment even on the way out inspired me.

After I am out, I receive a list of everything I am supposed to return, and soon after, a grapevine connected to the flying monkeys tells me they are broadcasting that I left my son's father with nothing and nowhere to go.

"This is between your dad and me; this is big people stuff; all you need to know is that we love you, and you will be taken care of," I tell my son as I drop him off at my sister's the day of the move.

It's awful, all that. The most horrible is watching the man I am leaving show up, sit down, and unfurl large blueprints of a canceled project on the coffee table in front of him in the center of the room at precisely the time I'd told him the helpers would arrive.

My brother asks me what the hell the man is doing when we are downstairs loading things in the truck. "He's pretending to work," I say.

"Aren't you going to say something?"

"I just want to get out," I say.

Back upstairs, six of us continue to move around the man, emptying the apartment. My brother stands over him and says, "Are you gonna help or what?"

This startles the man. He talks about Achille's heel.

"Whatever," my brother says, "you're in the way, and if you're not gonna help, get out of the way."

The man carries some things downstairs.

If you're not gonna help, get out of the way rings throughout my body, striking me as words it would have been good to say a long time ago.

"I have to tell you; I guessed you were moving out alone, even though you didn't tell me," a helping friend mentions hours later as we sit on the upstairs landing of the new home.

"Oh, God. You're right. I only told some family."

She looks at her husband, "And I forgot to tell him what I assumed."

He smiles. "I was a bit confused there for a while."

We laugh. The house fills with friends and family. I am resting my back against the kitchen sink when I look toward the front door and see my son walk in with my sister. I watch him look around with a relieved and surprised smile. Then he sees me. "This is a great place, Mom," he says as he walks toward me.

"Your room was the first one ready; go upstairs and look," I say. I can't remember if he didn't want to see the house or if I didn't have the time or heart to show it to him. It was hard to concentrate while separating from someone who pretended it wasn't happening while it was happening. Hard to say, "know you can go with your dad wherever he is going, and I will be okay with that and know you are always welcome with me" to our son in front of his father, but at least it was said in front of both.

My sister stacks Subway sandwiches on the table next to chips, salsa, and cold drinks set out by others and tells everyone to grab one. A cousin and a friend are stocking the kitchen cabinets and refrigerator. "Doesn't that bother you that they are making those decisions without you?" my sister asks on the patio.

"Nope," I say.

The first days are uneasy, and I receive many unkind messages. Then the phone rings with an invitation for a boat ride, and I am happy my son wants to join me. Stepping into the boat, I hear a splash. A friend says, "Oh, no, that was your phone."

I raise my hands in relief, "Yay!" It is a pleasure to imagine the toxic messages floating down the river and out to sea, far away.

"That has to be the best response I have ever seen from anyone who has lost their phone in the river," my friend says.

My son is already in the muddy water, searching for it. "Mom! How can you say that?"

"It's good to be free of it, babe. Don't worry. I'll get another one eventually," I say.

We motor out from the marina onto the breadth of the Mississippi. The baby–of a young woman I cared for as a baby–laughs in my arms as his mother–who cared for my son when he was a baby–chats with my son. My friend, the young woman's mother, hands me a glass of wine while the young woman's father drives the boat.

I watch my son unwind, smile, and laugh. He watches me water-ski. I love laughing, feeling loved, giving love, and letting my mind fly off with the turkey vultures.

After an August morning of trying to figure out how to pay for everything until my paycheck arrives in October,

and how to help my son get what he needs,

and how to get his father to pay his bills now coming through my bank account,

and after having gone to social services to see what help might be available there,

and there, having faced the choice of receiving help for a month's rent and gas money to get back and forth to work until my paycheck comes

—in exchange for participating in an employment workshop and giving social services my son's father's contact information "because he is responsible for half the support of your son, ma'am"—

or refusing the help to shield my son's father from pursuit by county officials,

I stand on the sidewalk of Main Street in the glaring sun, thinking of childhood shopping trips with my city grandma and how I never imagined this moment in my future.

It takes the fresh air to wake me up; I choose to take care of myself and my son rather than enable his father's nonfeasance.

I then learn that my son's father is living in a homeless shelter,

and I go back in and give the address to the authorities,

my body burning with embarrassment and shame.

Once home, I trudge upstairs toward my bedroom.

My son is in the long room and hears me coming.

"Mom," he calls out, and I look in. He is sitting on the couch, looking out the window. "It's so peaceful here," he says.

I let that sink in.

Seeing my son off for the first day of his last school year is bittersweet. He butters toast with his backpack on, and I see again the three-year-old he was going off to preschool. It amazes me that he will graduate from the same high school I did.

Before setting up my new office and attending meetings, I stop for a last swim before the pool closes for the season, slide down the mega slide, and–after a long pause at the edge–jump from the high dive.

At the university, I stand behind the French professor-on-leave's desk staring at boxes, books, and papers bulging from floor-to-ceiling shelves. I have reached my limit on dealing with other people's overwhelming stuff.

I walk down the hall, pop my head into the alchemist's office, and ask, "Do I have to take the office with the job?"

"No, in fact, she will be thrilled if you don't. I would like our department to start occupying some of the fourth floor if you want to move up there, you can. You will be away from everyone, though, and with the philosophy department."

"Perfect," I say.

It's lovely to be at the quiet end of the hallway with windows looking over the lawn and immense oak trees. I like being with philosophers and am thrilled to be invited to speak in one's classroom about my work.

"He told me he called your bluff," a woman says as she touches my arm at the first social event I attend after moving.

"Bluff?" I say. Then, as I stand there wondering what kind of person would say that and what type might repeat that, the sister at my side steers me in the opposite direction.

"That's so embarrassing," I say.

"It would only be embarrassing if you were still with him," she insists.

Opening the door to my other sister at two in the morning and listening to her stories about showing colleagues around town and her nomination for Best Hostess for Any Future Event is a joy.

She asks if she can stay with me, and as we lie in bed, I talk about my grief. "You have to draw a line in the sand," she says.

"Can I go to the beach and do that?" I ask. "The Mediterranean, say?"

It's awful how long it takes me to let go. Part of it is hope; part is exhaustion—it's already taken so much out of me to change my course this much, and I have a new job with new responsibilities and a son to care for in his last year of high school.

Decorating the new home exactly as I like is a great pleasure. Because I miss the sea so much, I decide to have a photo of my favorite spot overlooking the Mediterranean printed in a 40 x 60 format so I can frame it like a window. I hesitate when I realize how expensive the frame of my choice is. The saleswoman asks, "Would you like it?"

I look back at the photo and feel one of those mysterious arousals from the depths.

"Yes," I nod.

A clearing happens inside me,
  and I feel like I am standing at the altar
    of my life,
      feasting.

"I imagine you get more respect from the students in your French classes," a colleague says.

"Yes. Isn't it strange that they give less value to the mastery of their language than they do to the acquisition of another?"

"That is a skill our culture values; American culture does not value writing," she says. I wonder if that is true, and if so, why.

It is true that teaching French and advising the French club is more fun than I expected. French Club membership more than doubled under my supervision, and this makes me happy.

Also fun is horseback riding with a cousin, and a friend, who shared the same grade-school lunch table with me. We were tetherball champions, each other's rivals at the pole. Now, as adults, we ride horses into the sunset, share dinner, wine, and belly laugh like eight-year-olds.

"Eat grapes," the hostess says when I talk about how my mind sometimes gets the best of me. "They are supposed to help with obsessive thoughts."

On the way home, I buy a couple of pounds of them, then as soon as I enter the kitchen, I pour them into a bowl in the center of the table.

"If you want to know what is happening in the world, read the poets instead of the news," I tell two hundred fellow citizens as I introduce them to writers from far reaches of the planet. I read my work and translations of their work in tandem with them. This is one of the best nights of my life.

To give fellow foreign writers a tour of my hometown, to have dinner with them, to see the execution of the event pulled off so sweetly, with music and food selected by each writer, and to have old friends, new friends, family, and especially Mom and sister sitting right up front is pure joy, a profound homecoming.

During those first months in the new home, I often walk out on the porch at dawn to watch the ember glow of the sky over the river. On Fridays, my day off, I rest on the patio, enjoying the sun, the caw of a crow, a trill from an unfamiliar bird, and the occasional clunk of a walnut hitting the ground. I make two dreams come true when I buy a piano—one is for me to play, and the other is to hire a teacher for my son. One of the greatest joys in the new home is listening to him play like a natural. I wake to his music-making often and hear it intermittently throughout the day and night.

An advertisement with flying pink turtles under the words FOLLOW US TO GREAT REWARDS appears in the mailbox. I put it on the fridge.

Paused in front of the mirror, I play with the gray streak in my hair, touch the brown sunspot re-emerging on my cheek, and examine the crooked tooth in my mouth. I ponder covering, removing, and straightening things, then reentering the modeling world as a hot fifty-five or sixty-year-old, say. I wave at myself to check for arm flab.

Still okay.

A bunny hops through the snow, races across the backyard, then skids on the basketball court. I turn from the kitchen window and see movement—two people carrying firewood and piling it next to the glider on the front porch.

"It's an early Merry Christmas," the grade school friend with horses says, and I hug her. Then she introduces me to the love in her life.

I feel so happy as I drive to work, thinking of these hometown people, their kindnesses, and how they lift my heart.

"*Encore!*" the French class pleads after I teach them French swear words on this last day of classes before Thanksgiving.

"My mind's just shot," Mom says on the way back from my sister's the next day.

"Mine's close," I say.

"Oh, goody," she says, "we can lose it together."

"Write down the kind of man you would like to come into your life," a friend tells me via phone from the Field of Dreams farmhouse.

"I'm wary of men," I say as we say goodbye. I'm watching the fire.

"Come and take a look at this," the landlord calls from the kitchen. I see him lying on his back, looking up into the dishwasher. He shows me what is wrong and tells me how he will fix it. For a split second, I imagine lying on top of him.

To stave off any future impulse to jump a decent, handsome married man lying on the kitchen floor talking to me about dishwasher parts, I return to the fire and write about the kind of man I think I'd like to be with.

A long, precise list appears in front of me, and my hand goes to my mouth as if I have spoken too much. My fingers smell like nutmeg from cooking. I shake my head and turn my focus to work—on the *imparfait, plus que parfait,* and *subjonctif* lessons: These French tenses sound like ice cream treats and cocktails to me.

Later, at Mom's, when I joke about the way some of my attractive students make eyes at me, she scowls. "Now, don't get screwing around and get pregnant, that's all you need."

"If you work on the novel while there, I will," the alchemist says after I ask her to proctor a final exam so I can get a cheap ticket to Florida to visit a friend. She is pushing me to put *Lucy, go see.* out into the world. Although she translates alchemical texts and writes about alchemy, she doesn't call herself an alchemist. *I* call her the alchemist because she helps me transform into the writer I want to be, into who I am, the essence of me. That makes me feel good.

Poolside under the sun, I spend days swimming, reading, and revising another draft. As I breaststroke, I overhear a man telling his father, "Just because you are a white male, it doesn't mean the world is yours."

I love being with my friend, watching the sunset on Sanibel Island, and eating key lime pie at a pistachio-colored restaurant amid a row of pink, turquoise, and yellow bungalows. Her wise words soothe me when I receive texts of insult and blame. She helps me see more clearly, this woman who has known me since I was 12. "There are consequences to actions," she says, reminding me to focus on my own.

Pitch-dark, snow flying. My son and I celebrate the end of that stressful year with delicacies bought during a post-Christmas trip to Chicago with a sister and her kids. We feel like we are in Sitges again, sitting in front of the fire drinking cava, eating jamon ibérico on *pan con tomate*, French cheeses, Greek olives, and clementines. It is twenty-five below zero.

On most Sundays and sometimes other days, I go to Mom's and help her shower. I massage her, give her a pedicure or a facial, style her hair, do her makeup, and put her earrings in. It is increasingly challenging for her to do these things on her own, and it makes me feel good to make her feel and look good. Then we go out for a drive, visit family, or have a meal somewhere.

Sometimes I can't. Sometimes I want to stay home. She misses me then and calls and asks me to please come, and it is hard to say no, but sometimes I do.

Amid the difficulty of separation, work, and Mom's loneliness, it is easy to forget I am young.

A cousin comes to help with the car's battery and walks in carrying a pizza to share with my son and me. I know our grandma would be happy to see us together. When we were kids, our immediate families were often apart because of a feud between Grandma's sons and their father, supposedly about a strawberry patch. I remember when she talked about how family members were upset with her for talking to her son after he stayed away from his father's deathbed. "He's my flesh and blood," Grandma said, looking at me and holding herself, "how can I turn away from him?"

"Don't you think it's time to take the tree down?" my cousin, the son of Grandma's estranged son, asks as he enters the living room. "It's Valentine's Day, in case you didn't know."

"We might keep it up until Easter," my son says. I love seeing his playfulness emerge.

It's good to have family in the house. The three of us sit in front of the fire, eat, drink, tell stories, and laugh. We learn things about each other. My cousin looks at me as if he just remembered something good and asks, "Did you know I brought your dad a black raspberry pie days before he died? God, how happy that made him."

"That makes me happy, too," I say. "I still can't believe he's gone."

He nods knowingly. "The night my dad left this earth, I sat up straight out of my sleep in the middle of the night, swearing I heard him say, 'See you, son.' A few minutes later, the phone rang with the news that he was gone."

An international diplomat knocks on my Iowa door at the end of February. A year earlier, over winter break, I edited some of his extensive scholarly work in English, and afterward, he wrote that he would like to treat me to lunch in his beautiful city one day, to which I replied that it might be a while. I like remembering how I bought creams, lingerie, and other sensual luxuries with the money he paid me for the work. I was married when I did it and still am, but I no longer live with my husband. This man doesn't know that, but here he is to woo me, though he presents this grand journey like a casual visit on his way across the country. Despite my mention of the frigid cold, the remoteness of my hometown, and its lack of Michelin 3-star restaurants like those he boasted his hometown has, he flew to Chicago, rented a car, then drove to Dubuque.

He bows at the sight of me. We speak Spanish, English, and French; he signs a copy of the book I edited for him and offers it to me, and then we enjoy lunch and conversation and get to know a bit about each other in a seafood restaurant near the river. Afterward, I direct him to the city's points of interest.

When we drive by my childhood home, then up around the bend, I tell him to turn and go down the lane to the ancestral farm. I haven't been there since my husband offended the woman of the house via e-mail during the U.S. invasion of Iraq. I tried to stop him. She belittled the Swedish diplomat who verified there were no weapons of mass destruction in Iraq, and my husband criticized her. Now, a former colleague of that Swedish diplomat is driving me down the lane toward the farm.

"I think there is a place halfway down where we can turn around," I say. "I just want a view of it and to show you where my European ancestors made a home."

I am wrong; there is no turnaround spot, so we must go all the way to the house to get back up the hill. As we get close, the woman of the house comes out to see who is in her driveway and invites us in.

I introduce my guest, and as she and her husband chat with him about their European travels, I look up the stairs and see Dad again, pointing to the room he was born in and where his beloved grandmother died.

Throughout the house, I hear echoes of my grandmother giving birth to my father and the voice of the doctor who stayed with her through the night;

I imagine her mother helping her, family calling from the yard, and different rooms, aunts and uncles as children talking to each other, running up and down stairs, calling to their parents and grandparents.

I look out the kitchen window and see, covered in snow, the watermelon patch Dad loved to tend with his uncle, the spot he told me his mom had a pretty flower garden, and the brothers' batting practice and family picnic spot.

The home I grew up in, up on the hill, is framed by the window, as are the rolling pastures where I ran, rolled, and rode sleighs. Over the voices of the diplomat and the homeowners, I hear Dad's, telling me where the best walnuts are found and how he loved hunting with his great uncle when he was a boy.

Out of another window, though the trees are bare, I see Dad tugging a green apple from the branch and tossing it to me one August afternoon. "Eat that," he said. "It's good for you. I planted that tree with my dad."

"Do you think I could find a way to buy and live on the farm and write?" I'd asked then. "Maybe I could have a big flower garden and sell them at the market?"

"I think you'd need more than flowers, babe," he said.

From the bathroom window, I see Dad as a boy and young man and Grandpa as a young father planting potatoes where they would get the most sun, right there on the hillside. My daydreams about living here and writing seem as old as I am, yet that February day, an eery feeling about what I might find mingling with the spirits of that house, surprises me.

In front of the fireplace, the four of us talk about our travels, and the diplomat speaks about his work as an ambassador. A current passes through me as I look up at him. It feels like a nudge from the ancestors as if they are saying, "Go, see."

This, too, surprises me.

"One of the true aspects of who you are–a beautiful aesthetician–is a sense of lavishness, luxury, glamour, magnetics. I'm feeling an elongated longing for more ceremony and recognition of ceremony. Pizzaz. Let glamour be; that is part of the message coming through."

I usually take these sessions with the visionary lying down, this one, in early spring, upstairs in the long room, on the floor, on my back, listening through the speaker phone. "Glamour is a word that makes me wary," I say. "I prefer presence. Glamour sounds frivolous, not good for me."

"Glamour is not only superficial. You have deep glamour. And redefine what is good: this word is imprisoning you. This continual grading you are doing of yourself is degrading. Graduate yourself. Look at your ability to go, to accomplish, to receive. Look at your steely strength and resourcefulness. You are a living-your-dreams dreamer—a navigator between dreams and reality. There are bigger dreams to which you have not dared to give voice. And there is something very alchemical about you. Connect with the magician in you. You are a magical child in a woman's body with an innate connection to your desire. There is boldness in your essence–nothing is wasted, and everything is decorated.

This boldness has been dimmed, covered up. Welcome acquired wisdom. No mustering, no working at it; it is more about allowing it than being comfortable with it. Have a coming-out party of who you are right now."

I listen. It all makes sense and gives me hope.

"Something has been compressed; the substance is still there and ready to expand. Holding it all together is not your job. A new circle of people matching your strength, and comfort with that, is coming into your life. Acknowledge the hard work you have already done. I am seeing the birth of a fiery but funny dragon, but it's not a baby dragon; it is more advanced–a birth in mid-evolution–birthing the conglomeration of who you are, regathering, reconvening with that part you cut deals with."

Parts of me I gave up to get something else–no immediate examples come, but I can feel the truth in this.

"Follow the impulse to sparkle. It is where your spirit has been lying in a lost connection, lost awareness of connections. Dreams are still there, and new ones appear every day. A ton of them, I can't even grasp how many."

It's good to hear about dreams in a place where I let go of a big one and worry all might go with it. I've been hiding to protect myself from pain, slogging through, and focusing on being a good mom, daughter, and professor. Unsure if I am doing well in any of these roles. I miss being me, a daring, fun, and funny woman, and I miss the sun and sea.

After the session, I wander for sparkle equipment. I have a blast getting a great deal on a floor-model vanity at Pier 1, aided by the poet's sister, who now works there. At a boutique on Bluff Street, I select luscious creams and oils, also on sale. As I pay, the saleswoman says, "I know you and your parents. I have never in my life met a man as neat as your father. You look like him. You must miss him. I babysat your cousins and knew all your aunts, uncles, and grandparents."

I open my mouth, but no words come out.

"Your mom called me when you were going off to Chicago and New York to model to ask my advice because I had modeled, too, here at Roshek's department store. I worked in the clothing department. I knew your family well. Will you model for us in one of our fashion shows?"

"Maybe," I say.

"Please accept that pleasure. Please let yourself be glamorous. And please go so I can live it vicariously. How many fifty-year-old women get offered tickets to Europe?" the alchemist says when I tell her the diplomat is inviting me to visit in June.

"Maybe my husband and I can still work things out," I say.

The alchemist looks at me like she'd like to write her words on a gigantic sign and put it on my wall. "You are never going to work things out."

I look out the office window and say, "I'd just like to see him do more for our son."

"I'd like to see him tied up and forced to watch you making out with another man for hours," she answers.

At home and on the phone, I tell another friend, "I keep hoping he will wake up."

"Or maybe you will," she says.

"We have to find her," an aunt nods toward me while addressing the family at a Mother's Day picnic, "a boyfriend."

"I'm still married," I say.

She shoos my answer with her hand. "You can get rid of that with a piece of paper."

I would like to know what kind of boyfriend my family would come up with for me. I refrain from asking.

"I go to Barcelona often. I can pick up your things and bring them here. I have a lot of extra storage room. There are no strings attached, I promise you. You can even ask me to go to Sweden when you come to pick up your things if you want—and I will," the diplomat writes in April after I mention I need to get my things out of a friend's attic.

I don't know what else to do, so I believe him and accept his offer.

In May, he again invites me to visit. "You would have your own bedroom and office with a balcony in my home, and you could organize your things. Walking on the beach, swimming, dining in Michelin 3-star restaurants, and visiting Spain and France could be exhilarating."

The word *exhilarating* stirs me. While planting seeds for morning glories, nasturtiums, and belles de nuit, I ponder the invitation. When I walk inside to wash my hands, another message arrives: "I would be pleased to offer you a round-trip flight from Dubuque whenever you like."

A flight to exhilaration and back is tempting.

The following week I feel myself sparkling as I talk about writing to a group of twelve women in a private back room of a Belgian restaurant in Galena. With the money I earn, I sign up for a writing workshop led by a writer I admire, to be held in Door County, Wisconsin, at the end of July. I feel like I'm moving further into the life I want to live.

Flying helicopter seeds from maple trees patter on the roof of the back patio and spin lightly to the ground.

"It is a long way to travel for a date and a long date at that," I write to the diplomat and accept his invitation. I mention that I am still married and un-sure how that will work out and ask if he needs to know more about that.

"The only thing I need to know is your passport number and birthdate so I can book your ticket," he answers.

We celebrate our son's graduation. It is awkward, but I find joy in seeing my son happy. I make all the effort and am so glad for our son to have his parents and grandmother there, and I can feel his appreciation in the long, strong hug he gives me at the end of what was also an awkward day.

I finish grading for the semester and then accept translating a book as summer work. At the airport, an acquaintance asks where I am headed.

"Far," I say over my shoulder and wave.

During a layover at Barajas, I enjoy a breakfast I love—*zumo de naranja fresco, una flauta con tomate y* jamon serrano, and café con leche—while watching a man talking on a cellphone and gesturing dramatically as if the person can see him. I wander amid Sisley products in Duty-Free, and a hostess offers to do my makeup, then points to a chair like those I sat in for decades on set. As she works on my face, I close my eyes and hear *"Mira arriba,"* which means look up, which I've heard countless times from make-up artists, and which brings tears to my throat.

After walking away from that embellishment, a salesman presents me with a red box of Valor chocolates and asks if I want to try one. I want to tell him I was in one of their commercials, but I feel shy. All the Spanish years tumble through my mind and heart in this airport I know well, in which I was usually traveling to or from Sitges. I remember how while living there, I dreamed of a home in Iowa with a porch, fireplace, and garden. The dream did come true, I note, albeit with slight alterations.

On a terrace overlooking islands, roofs, and hilltops, I sit at a table with a flute of cava sparkling in my hand. The diplomat carefully lifts one of my favorite fishes, the gilt-head bream, onto the plate in front of me, then adds scoops of other sides I love. The fresh cool air and the moody sky are exhilarating. During the meal, the diplomat keeps my glass filled with Godello and afterward offers me a bowl of cherries, a small cup of freshly brewed espresso, and bites of chocolate. I am served my favorite things. A year or more will pass before I wonder if he read through the diaries in the boxes he moved for me.

"How do you feel?" He asks. "Are you tired? Would you perhaps like to ride and visit nearby villages?"

I'm delighted.

The following day and many other mornings, he says, "If you agree, I will have the housekeeper pack us a lunch, and we can take it to the beach, have a walk and a swim, then later we can take a drive to another village or perhaps another country, and then, after that, we can have a nice dinner at a fish restaurant? Would that be okay with you?"

I agree each time.

"Just leave your bed; the housekeeper will make it," he says when he sees me smoothing the sheets.

"That's hard for me."

He raises his eyebrows.

"Okay, I will try."

I see photographs of his wife, who died four years earlier, almost everywhere I turn. The urn holding her ashes sits on a shelf above his head as we have breakfast.

Little to no sleep mixed with jet lag concoct a delirium I try to keep at bay.

I listen to the diplomat talk about his wife at a tall table outside a tapas bar in the old city center. "Separation and divorce are often deprived of the same consideration death receives from people," I say. "Yet, there is inconsolable grief in all these cases. So much here is reminding me of the life I used to have." I am tired of holding back tears.

He places a plate of calamari in front of me. "Would you like to visit another beautiful place?"

I nod, eat, drink, then take the arm he offers as we walk to the car.

He drives us through a mountain pass where vast green meadows stretch toward a sparkling blue bay, then parks near ruins, and we walk. Standing near a crumbling column, he looks at me and says, "You may never have the A relationship you felt you had or that your dream was, but maybe you can have an A- or a B+; that is still not bad."

His gentleness moves me even though I find the grading of relationships weird.

Maybe it is letting my tears spill that softens me. Or it could be the ease in his body–its movement, length, strength, and tone. His chivalrous behavior. That evening I move closer to him.

After more beautiful and relaxing days, I eventually go to his bed.

The first warm day, while he writes, I walk along the shore. When he arrives, we stroll hand in hand. I love the way bodies brighten and synchronize in movement after making love. We dive. When the salt hits my tongue, a cry I muffle in the depths rises from my gut.

Sometimes I realize how much I missed something when I live it again.

"You have a tremendous sexuality," the diplomat says as we lie in the sun.

I murmur in agreement, quietly amazed by the extent of my excitement with him. He is more generous outside of bed than in. I learn that exterior generosity can be exciting, too.

"The neighbors probably think that my wife has come back," he says when I stand up from the lounge chair on the upper terrace that afternoon.

Then he leads me to his storage space and opens a long, narrow, clean space filled with the contents of my sanctuary in Sitges. I look at it all and touch some of it.

"We can look at this later. I see this is emotional, perhaps a bit too much for you right now," he says, and he is right.

On the summer solstice, we climb over French dunes, then plant a parasol into a vast beach. The diplomat reads an American editorial to me in Spanish after asking permission to rest his head on my side. What he reads is funny, and we laugh. We eat my favorite sandwiches, *bocadillo con tomate y tortilla de patatas*, swim, play in the waves, walk, and rest. I snap photos of the blood-orange sun reflecting off the lapping waves at sunset.

"This is what we used to do," the diplomat says as we stroll along the shore. "This is the way we liked to spend our days here."

I could say the same thing he did about the day, but I have been telling myself, most of the day–and mainly when he rested his head on my side, and I was so pleased he'd asked first–that this day, experience, man, is different, even though I have been in the same position with others.

A bit later, as we rest on a pier, I say something. "You know what? This is the way we used to spend our days often, too. Exactly like this."

He is quiet, then.

The next day, the housekeeper rubs her arms and tells me she has shivers coming into the room where I am packing because of how much I remind her of the lady of the house.

Okay, I look different, that I can see with my own eyes, but I must feel like her. Grief is long and perhaps never-ending, so I imagine it is a question of time. I am in no hurry, happy to know I can feel affection for another, glad to be treated well, the wifely comparisons aside, and happy to taste an international life again. It's a delight to be with a helpful "solutions man," as he calls himself.

He checks in to ask how it's going. "Don't worry," he says. "I will take whatever you cannot to the post office after you go. Let us go now and have a nice dinner."

B ack in Dubuque, Mom and I have dinner at the Europa Café. "I am going to finish the marriage, Mom. I'm done," I say.

"Whoops," she says, which triggers a rush of unexpected tears.

I rush away from the table. While sitting on the toilet with my head in my hands, a woman opens the stall I forgot to lock, and I hear, "Whoops," again.

This time I laugh.

Mom calls the following day. "Oh, good, you're there," she says, "I thought maybe you left the country."

A chalcedony sky, a quiet train bridge. Cars on the motor bridge four hundred yards away. Ducks fly then skid to join each other on the beach below. It smells like dry mud. I look south, picturing New Orleans, and remember the drive there along the river, when I was pregnant and far from imagining Dubuque as the end of the line. A year has passed since I moved— twenty-seven since first sight.

"I am finished with the marriage," I say.

It is all uneasy, painful, and sad, and I am proud I keep myself together. Then I walk down the grassy hill toward the car without looking back.

I swim for a long time the following morning.

After watering flowers and pulling weeds, I eat fresh tomatoes and pesto on the back patio.

A text message arrives from the diplomat, wanting to fix a visit date. The rest of the exchange goes like this:

I am unable to make that decision right now.

Why not?

I told my husband I was finished with our marriage yesterday.

I hope he does not try to seduce you.

While I squint at the screen, trying to understand the root of the diplomat's hope, a new text message confirms the diplomat's assumption.

I go back to bed and stay there until dusk.

Hours later, to respond to the attempt at seduction, I write I am not in a position to do that. I want to remove the *not* and find other soft words for refusal, but I am tired, and the word position appeals to my sense of humor.

"I hope you are not divorcing your husband for me," the diplomat says in the following days when I finally answer the phone.

"I'm doing it for me," I say, bothered by his presumption.

"You saw the best of me this summer, and I must tell you I can be a real son-of-a-bitch."

"I have eyes of my own. I'll figure that out," I answer.

"Get out of town. And tell the Frenchman to take his ass to Paris and write poetry and to quit sending you those fucked-up messages and shoving all those letters in your mailbox," a friend says when I talk about what's going on.

After I hang up the phone, I glance out the front window, then look again. My son's father is sitting under an oak tree across the street, staring at the house. His brow is furrowed, his jaw tense.

Had he knocked or rung the bell without me hearing it? I wonder as I stand there, feeling like a tightly closed clam. I shake my body then walk toward the kitchen and stand in it, trembling, feeling what feels like an ancient primal fear as I move like an animal looking for shelter in my home. This confuses me, and I go upstairs and stretch in the long room, reminding myself that I am an adult woman who can care for herself.

After dusk, when I look, he is gone. I sit on the glider as I love to do when it is fully dark, now hyper-vigilant. After no answer to my texts to my son, I call a brother, then Mom. "Here," she tells me softly, to say he is sitting nearby.

The next afternoon I glance out the window and see my son's father is back, furiously pacing the sidewalk on the other side of the street, flapping his shirt open and closed like a peacock's wings. I call a friend who says she will be right over.

When I open the door, I see two policemen standing over my son's father, once more at the base of the tree. My friend follows me into the kitchen and stands nearby as I double over. "A woman stopped me on the street on the way here to tell me she called the police because she saw a man acting strangely in front of the school," she says.

"Jesus," I say.

"Hardly," she answers.

It feels good to laugh a little.

There is another knock on the door. Two police officers. One says, "Excuse us, ma'am, could we come in to ask you some questions?"

I nod, step back, and he points to the police officers across the street, leaning over my son's father. "Is that your husband?"

"Yes, but no; Last week, I told him I want a divorce. I also told him I could not see him for a while."

"Is this his house?"

"No."

"Has he ever lived in this house?"

"No."

"How long have you been separated?"

"A year."

The policeman's eyes widen. "So, would it be correct to tell him this is not helping?"

"Yes."

That night, a sister-in-law who knows I want to talk to my son sends me a message: Your son is sleeping here. You might like to come out and get some eggs in the morning.

Around nine, I drive to my brother and his wife's with an empty egg carton and a box of donuts. I set the donuts on the picnic table before heading to the chicken coop at the end of the long yard. It is quiet, and the glistening grass tickles my bare feet and ankles as I walk, then lift the barbed wire and crouch to pass through the fence. I love finding warm eggs alone in the nests, much more than reaching under the hens to take them.

On the way back through the yard, I feel fortunate to give my boy hard news on land where we both have had much fun and love.

I set a dozen eggs at the end of the picnic table and watch sulphur butterflies play tag above the grass. When my son comes outside, I say good morning, offer the donuts and point at the freshly cut wood stacked nearby and the copper-colored geometric designs in the core of the split trunks. "Aren't they pretty?" I ask.

He nods. He's been avoiding me for days now, knowing I want to talk.

"Babe," I say, watching him closely, "what I have to say is brief, and I wish your dad could tell you with me, but he said he could not."

My son stays put; he's an adult now, I tell myself as I watch him play with the grass with his toes as I do.

"Your father and I are going to divorce," I say.

He looks toward the pasture, then the sky, as if a far-off plane is now in sight.

"What I want you to know and remember is that we love you and you are a child of love."

The news enters and sinks. His relief that a decision has finally been made and spoken is evident in his posture.

"That's what I've wanted to tell you these last few days. I will only talk more about it if you want to," I say.

He is quiet. We look at the designs on the chopped wood again, and he moves toward them, then touches and traces them. "These *are* cool, Mom," he says.

"I am going to go for a swim at your aunt's in Iowa City and then listen to some live music at a winery nearby. Would you like to come along?"

"That sounds fun."

His uncle walks out the back door with work boots in his right hand and stands in the middle of the stairs at a spot that reminds me of our grandma's fall on the ice. I see at least ten dead relatives and us, as children, going up and down the stairs around him. "What's going on?" he asks with a smile that has our parents in it.

I lift the donuts.

"I never say no to a donut." He turns to his nephew. "What are you doing today? You wanna make some money?"

"Yeah," my son says.

"I'm going to bail hay. If you want, you can come."

"I'd love that," he says.

"I'll go home and get you the clothes you need and drop them off on my way to Iowa City," I say.

My son hugs me then, and I can feel his heartbeat.

I whisper "I love you" into my brother's ear as I hug him.

"How was your trip?" a sister asks as we dance after swimming. For a split-second, I think, what trip?

It's only ten days since I got back from Europe.

That night my son calls. "Mom, I met a cousin of yours today. A really nice guy. We worked on his farm and then hung out with him." I say my cousin's name. "Yeah, that's him. I had a great day, Mom. I was calling to tell you about it because I knew it would make you feel good."

"It does, babe. I've been making plans to visit northern Wisconsin in a couple of weeks; would you like to come along?"

"Yeah, sure, just give me the dates, and I will ask at work tomorrow."

s I wait for the light to cross Clinton Street in Iowa City on a sultry July afternoon, a message from the diplomat appears on my phone.

I read it out loud at lunch with a friend. "How does one say no to this— Would you like to end the year with me in Vienna and then spend some of the first days of the new year in Paris?"

"Oh, dear, don't say no."

Later, over glasses of wine, another friend advises, "Your relationship with your son now will determine where he spends his holidays. Move into a new relationship with him. And for whatever it is worth, I was thrilled when my mother finally got rid of my father and lived an exciting life for herself."

I am excited to get out of town with my son. The night before we leave, we ride horses in open pastures under a full moon with the friend who brought me firewood. I stay behind to watch the two of them talking and my son smiling atop a beautiful horse on a summer night.

To see one's child happy might be the best happiness.

I was unaware before I had a child that when I did, my happiness would depend on his.

It is also difficult for me to be happy when my mother is unhappy.

These three bodies—the one I came from, mine, and the one I gave life to—all connect to one happiness.

Driving north toward Devil's Lake, electrified deeply and quietly, I breathe easier every mile. Memories of driving my son to Andorra to see snow and mountains when he was 2, and through the Pyrenees to see the castle in Carcassonne when he was 4, mingle with the present journey. I catch myself reaching down to take his hand as we walk toward a coffee shop in Madison and realize once more that he is a young man now, taller than me, and soon a college student. We have fun choosing music and comedy CDs for the trip in a bookstore, then drive on, laughing and singing.

About an hour later, we arrive at a sandy beach near rugged cliffs. The clear water reveals a pebbled lakebed—we have it all to ourselves for swimming, climbing, and relaxing until the sun sets.

At the Wisconsin Dells, we crack up in the front seats of a high-speed boat as the driver increases speed, and spins us around, rock-and-roll blasting on the sound system.

We meander on county and state highways, and I turn the wheel over to my son, who drives most of the trip. I like watching him behind the wheel while I relax in the passenger seat, fully taking in the scenery without worrying about veering the car toward whatever catches my eye.

I love how he opens up and talks to me as he drives.

At Eau Claire, I say, "Dad often talked about how much he loved hitting a home run into the pines here," then direct my son to the island and field, Carson Park, where I imagine Dad as a young man in uniform, filing out of a bus, running onto the ball diamond.

"'Hell, I'd rather play baseball than eat' is one thing your grandpa often said," I say as we cruise along Half Moon Lake toward the Chippewa River. We spot a picnic table and stop and eat chips and drink shandies from the cooler at dusk on that fresh summer night.

In Hayward, near a train bridge, I tell my son to pull into the driveway of a log cabin sort of motel with wooden benches next to each room's door. I step inside the main office and speak to the German owner, who has space for us, a room with paneled interiors and old-fashioned wooden beds. We get brats from a stand across the street, then watch tv and relax before sleep.

In Bayfield, friends from Dubuque I've known all my life take us for walks along Lake Superior and to Madeline Island. They feed us cheeseburgers from their grill and freshly picked cherries from the nearby fields on their screened-in porch, where we watch bears visiting the yard.

Then we head east amid tall pines on a long stretch of road with only us on it, royal blue sky, milky clouds, James Taylor on repeat, windows down. Pancakes and eggs near the Chequamegon National Forest. We get lost in the north woods with no map or cellphone coverage, then follow our instincts and find a way out. We pass Green Bay at dusk, then park in front of a motel in Algoma. After skipping stones on Lake Michigan, I order fried chicken from a nearby restaurant, and we sit outside our door on the balcony passageway, eating and watching the moon on the lake.

At Egg Harbor the next day, we arrive at a condo a friend offered me for a few nights. While I attend a writing workshop, my son drives around exploring the area and later will take me to places he thinks I will like.

"What is invisible in your work yet essential to it?" is one question the workshop director asks.

Swimming. Flying in water. Disappearing in water. Being held by water. The buoyancy. The rhythm. I write like I swim and sometimes as I swim.

My son and I watch sunsets, eat meals outside, and laugh at *The Minion*s at a drive-in theater.

At the tip of the peninsula, where it looks like the edge of the world, each in a kayak, we slip through reeds, listen to and watch loons, and occasionally wave to each other.

At Fish Creek Beach, in the lake, he holds me in the air like I used to hold him. We eat ice cream in Ephraim, then cheeseburgers on the waterfront at sunset. That night, back in the condo, my son asks, "How do people make enough money to afford some of these places we have been in, Mom?"

"Different ways, babe. There is certainly financial benefit in staying in one place and job for decades. Hard work, in one way or another, is often the answer. Sometimes inheritance, sometimes marriage. Or sometimes like me right now, on credit, in installments."

He nods and looks lost. I wish I could comfort him.

Throughout those days, we stay close to each other, sing along to music, enjoy the beauty, eat well, sleep. Neither of us wants to talk about the end of our family.

Red coneflowers, purple bell flowers, pink phlox, and white hibiscus thrive when we return. The cardinals have built a nest in the third cedar tree. I do laundry and prepare lunch, remembering the days with the diplomat and wondering about the possibility of a life with him—one without domestic tasks—only writing and pleasure. This is what he is tempting me with via numerous calls and gifts.

When I take breaks from translating, I read Terry Tempest Williams's book about women being birds.

A crow screeches.

A squirrel works on an early walnut.

With my eyes closed on the acupuncturist's table, I see my son on a white horse, moving through the mud in a forest. A hoof catches, and he is off the horse, trying to free its foot from the ground. He is blond, like when he was a boy.

How to relieve the suffering, my son's and mine? This is a constant question and aim. How to move forward? How to honor his father without seeing or being with him or endorsing his neglect? How to keep my son whole when his life is split? How to love and forgive me?

I host a sizable going-away-to-college party for my son, which is uncomfortable and, again, awkward for me because I invite his father for my son's sake. I am rewarded by my son's noticeable relief and pride as he watches me calmly say, "This is our son's night; this is all about him," when his father tries to engage me in distracting conversation.

The following day, my son leaves with his father on a trip.

When he returns, it will be time for him to go to college.

"You look different and skinny," Mom says when I visit.

"Maybe it is the quiet work and the swimming," I say.

I stand at her side in the doctor's office, singing and holding her hand as he inserts two needles in her nose to numb it, then slices cancer from it, cleans the blood covering her face, and stitches it up.

How am I standing this, I wonder.

I read more about when women were birds—the importance of a community of women, how it is our speech that saves us, our own lips, not a prince's—and about the risk we take of losing our souls when we disregard our intuition.

I feel even more akin to the author when I read her words about how women and writers live outside and inside simultaneously.

I mention this to a friend, adding, "The man I shared my life with tried to stop me from writing, telling me, 'you cannot be in the train and watching it at the same time,' and I used to argue that I could, that I was capable of both living and writing my life—"

"He told you to stop writing?"

"I even tried to stop," I say, "but I found it impossible. I learned that writing, in some ways, is like breathing for me; it keeps me alive."

"Well, there is something you could thank him for, finding that out," she says.

The lawyer's e-mail tells me there is no response to the petition for dissolution. Summer is almost over. Another summer the novel lies untouched. "I wanted to do more of my own work this summer," I lament by telephone.

"You are doing your own work," the visionary reminds me.

We do a spectacular session that deserves a story of its own, replete with flamingos, dancing peanuts, slides, grandmothers walking on stage, and a clean-up crew. At one point, I feel like the Statue of Liberty, and it seems I am lying in an inflatable circular pool, like a child's pool, and it's too small for me. Then I look ahead and see a troll under a bridge nearby watching me.

My son and his roommate are assigned to a co-ed Writer's Hall. "That's cool; everyone here is a writer?" I ask as I read the quotes taped to some doors. "How did that happen?"

"We were grouped by interests, Mom. I think it's weird. Probably boring."

"Writers are fascinating, well, some of them," I say, then see female names. "Women and men on the same floor? What about showers?"

"They are pods. Everyone goes into their pod, Mom."

"Pod?"

"You can go, Mom. I've got this now. Thanks, Mom."

Though I am sad to say goodbye to more than eighteen years of togetherness, I feel freedom surge in me as I walk the city afterward, meeting friends, then staying overnight with a niece.

Still, I delay the return to an emptier home, a quiet ping pong table and piano, and walls filled with photos of my son's life, still affixed since his party.

C hipmunks scamper up limestones in the golden light. I prune a transla- tion and the garden and prepare fall classes. I enjoy moving around the city, knowing resistance to divorce proceedings is far away.

The lowering sun burnishes the Illinois riverbanks. After leaving a political rally for the person who will become our next president, a friend and I walk together. "Can you believe that? Well, we tried. We gave it a listen," she says.

"My favorite part was when the maintenance guys rolled out the steel di- viders to make the room look smaller and fuller and how that made more noise than that awful woman introducing him did, even when she raised her voice," I say.

She chuckles. After a bit, she says, "You seem to be breathing easier."

"I think this is the first time I have had a relaxing walk along the river in a year," I say. "It feels like coming home again."

"Don't you see? You are regaining your nature. You are coming back to who you are," the alchemist says when she stops in my office. It's a good thing I am unaware of how long that will take.

That night I feel like I am coming out of an embryonic curl as I dance to the radio in the kitchen and prepare a delicious dinner. The flickering of the candle captures my attention, as does the turning toward fall. I think about how I curled into myself to protect myself. I stretch now, determined to open. I celebrate the completion of two different translations, and I wonder about the diplomat's most recent text, asking if he can come and see me from mid-October to mid-November.

I say yes.

Drinking morning coffee on the porch, I watch my niece pull into my driveway, as she does on school days. I love to see her and her kids smiling at me. I love hugging them. Her daughter gives me a peck on the cheek and then goes to class across the street. Her toddler boy asks for my son.

"He is at college now," I say.

He looks perplexed and rushes upstairs to look for his cousin, the word college meaning nothing to him. My niece and I chat until he returns with a ping-pong paddle and a frown.

He grins as I offer him a bowl of cereal.

He looks like Dad.

These moments are pure joy.

"The man thinks I can only divorce him with his agreement," I tell a friend.

"Does he know he's in America?" she asks.

How to capture the brightness of the nasturtiums? That golden, orange, and redness, the way they unfurl? Hummingbirds stick their noses in them, usually around four in the afternoon. *Les capucines,* I say to myself, because I love the French word for them.

I first learned their name when I saw them tumbling from balconies in Sitges. *Caputxeta,* in Catalan.

I taste nasty in the word *nasturtium,* which seems unfit for this flower.

That fall, I eat them in salads and often want to roll around in them in the back garden.

Before the first frost, I cut them, and place vases filled with them in every room of the house.

Making love in my bedroom; cooking and enjoying meals, music, and candlelight with the diplomat; introducing him to American late-night television and laughing together; him bringing me lunch to my office; sharing meals on the back patio at home in the mid-autumn sun; taking day trips in the region; driving further to watch horses lengthen and stride in the final stretch at Keeneland amid the bright yellow, orange, and russet colors of fall, black barns, and green grass—these are pleasures.

News that the dissolution is postponed because the defendant's lawyer has dropped him; news that a friend's mother has died in Spain; another friend calling, whispering she has hopefully six months to live, and asking if I will speak at her celebration of life—these things are hard.

At a bookstore café between Kentucky and Iowa, the diplomat asks, "Do you know the ten most important authors in the U.S.?"

"What do you mean by important?" I ask.

This question bothers him. I can tell by the look on his face.

"A professor at Yale says the most important writers are male because there were just no women good enough to compete with them," he tells me, and I laugh.

At this point, I have agreed to a European trip at the end of the year, and a spring visit from him, which includes travel with him to California. I'm weighing my options.

The night before he leaves, he makes me dinner. "I hope she is not watching," he says, looking to heaven. "She would be very jealous because I never did that for her. She was a great homemaker, very neat and clean." He sweeps his thumb across the top of the refrigerator, then gives me a dusty thumbs up as he says, "For example, she would never have allowed this."

"I would have thrown the guy out the minute he ran his finger across the top of my fridge," a friend says later.

I shrug. "I was happy he took a sponge and cleaned it."

"Did you open some other cupboards then and say, what would she have done with this?" another friend asks.

Despite annoyances, it is hard to be alone again after he leaves. I do miss him, but maybe it is the shock of aloneness anew.

Three students fail to turn in a paper yet still show up in my office at their designated private meeting time to discuss it. One asks, "Isn't it hard to teach something people do not care about?"

I nod.

"I keep wondering if students' carelessness is my fault. It seems like the same problem I had in my marriage, this thinking their lack of motivation could mean my failure at inspiration," I say to the alchemist.

She takes a deep breath and shakes her head. "It's wonderful the way you ask questions. Stay curious, but please don't stress about this. You're memorable. It might be ten years from now when one of them sees what you gave them. Don't let them beat you down. Don't lose your magic here."

What she means is to keep trusting myself. I think that's the magic.

I could have asked, but I like hearing a superior say I have magic, so I quietly savor it.

The way the snow falls–covering everything in a gentle fluttering way– makes me wish it could do that with my life. It's the first snowstorm of 2015. My son is home for his Thanksgiving break. We dance in the kitchen as he makes brunch, and I bake a pecan pie for the meal we will share with my sisters and Mom. We go to a farm and select a tree for Christmas.

We light a fire, listen to Christmas music, and decorate the tree that night. "Mom, you know how people say money can't buy happiness? I think money is important."

"It is, babe. We need it to live. And it can provide support and security, and that helps happiness. I like to think about the language around money–it's called legal tender. And I like the slang word–dough–for it because it's what we make and create with money that is interesting. It's a medium of exchange and currency and only a measure of value in the marketplace. Circulation of it makes it more available. Dad used to say capitalism only works if people share, for example. I think it means different things to different people, and I sense many people are unaware of that, and that's why there is so much weirdness around it. Beliefs about it can be obstructive and even enslave people. It seems to create more fear than happiness in lots of folks. But it can be exchanged for stability, education, pleasure, ease, freedom, and time, yet there are other ways to have those things without paying money for them. It can't replace or buy love and peace, and those are a couple of things that are more important than it. I think it's best to appreciate, enjoy, and use it to live well but not to worship it or greedily hoard it. Anyway, I'm saying these things while I am still trying to find my way with it," I say as I hang the sailboat ornament he chose on Madeline Island.

I love lying in bed saying, "I love you" toward his room and hearing, "I love you, too, Mom," float toward mine.

"I want to make more of a life for myself before I live with someone again," I tell the diplomat by phone.

"But that is hard," he says, as reason enough to give up on it.

I am silent, tired of repeating myself on this issue.

Snow falls, and everything is white again, surreal. I call Mom.

"I have no idea what to do with myself," she says. "Are you coming to see me?"

"I'm trying to figure out how to describe the smell of geraniums. Powdery green?"

"It's almost Christmas, and you are thinking about geraniums?"

"I'm sitting next to them. I brought them inside in the fall and have them in the windows upstairs. Some have buds about to open."

"Come over here and get in bed and sleep with me," she says.

"Mom, you know I like having my own house and bed to sleep in, but I will come over for a while," I say.

I rarely stay overnight. I invite her to my house, but it's uneasy for her because all the bedrooms are upstairs, and it's difficult for her to climb and come down. I like bringing her over to hang out, even though she has told me she doesn't like my house. A brother suggests she live with me. I feel that would be wrong for both of us. Where she is, she can walk out of her apartment and mingle with people, and move about independently within the residence. She likes that. It's the only autonomy she has left.

"What are you doing here?" a student asks when he drops off his final paper. "Take off. Get out of here."

Another raises his hand in the classroom. "How come you never told us you were in a movie with The Hoff?"

I open my palms. "What does that have to do with the instruction of research writing?"

"Come on, tell us."

I show some pictures and tell stories about my modeling and acting careers. They all sit straighter in their seats and look at me more curiously.

"That earned me more respect and attention from the class than the PhD," I tell the alchemist when we meet at a Mexican restaurant we like.

"Listen," she says, after we laugh, "because of these massive state budget cuts, and because you are a recent hire, you will probably get a call in January telling you that you will not be offered a contract for next fall."

I sip more of the margarita in front of me. I'm disillusioned with universities—the uninterested students, the students overtaxed with jobs due to the expense of education, the grade inflation that goes along with the rise in tuition, certain ridiculous hierarchies, many lifeless, sad professors, condescending colleagues, and those telling me to pass students if they are failing so I can fill the next level's classroom the following semester, the administration making loads more than educators—and, overall, the way it all feels like a big business and an insider's club. Of course, exceptions exist, but getting out sounds nice. "That's okay," I say.

"You are by far the easiest person I've had to tell. I thought you might be happy because I have the feeling you might be moving back to Europe."

"It's tempting, but I'm focused on how to find more time for my writing here first."

"Anyway, the system is so screwed up," she says. "They are slashing the budget because they have to, but what will happen is they will see they slashed too much and will be calling you in July, asking you to come back in August."

"I have time," I say. "I'll figure something out." I already know I will say no if they call.

The diplomat texts from a train telling me he is thinking of asking me to marry him, but he is not ready yet.

Silence is my response, after considering good for a long while, then wondering if the arrogance apparent to me may be a question of language. I am arrogant without knowing it sometimes, so I give him the benefit of the doubt.

The winter solstice. Magic and stew with the alchemist and her husband, who serves us warm tea before playing the harp and piano for us.

Then Christmas.

My son is home.

Festive visits to family and friends.

Mom in my home, making extra effort climbing the stairs, sleeping over, and the three of us together Christmas morning, watching holiday shows, drinking coffee, and eating cookies.

Then, a visit to the Museum of Science and Industry in Chicago with my son, an Italian dinner, and a night in a nice hotel before he drops me at the airport the following morning.

"I've canceled the trip to Paris," the diplomat says when I arrive. "That's okay," I say.

"Why don't you want to come and live with me in Europe? You love Europe," he asks in Vienna, on the Gloriette Arch at Schönbrunn Gardens.

Looking out over the snowy palace grounds, remembering running through them one April decades before, I say, "I have some dreams I want to fulfill before settling into another couple."

He pulls his head back in surprise and repulsion and says, "Certainly, do not let me stop you from following your dreams."

I am often breathless on the way to the opera, restaurants, and museums as he pulls me to match his pace. Sometimes I let go of his hand and slow to my own; this bothers him.

Over a late supper, he talks about what he wants in a woman concerning culture, languages, body, beauty, sex, conversation, and interest in horse racing and opera.

As he talks, it occurs to me. "You've kept a chart, haven't you? You listed women, checked off boxes, and counted scores, didn't you?"

He nods. "But, you—I could not fit all of you in my chart."

He watches as I crack up. "Why are you laughing so hard?"

"I'm off the charts," I say.

"We'd like to hear what she has to say," the Epiphany luncheon's host declares after the diplomat talks over me.

I open my mouth, and he speaks over me again, so I cover his mouth with my hand.

"It will take more than that to stop him," a guest says.

I shrug, then sip more cava.

"I think I used to see you on the television," a woman across the table says.

I nod.

"And in Sitges. Didn't you live in Sitges?"

I nod again.

"You can come here and live and do your creative writing," the diplomat says, and the way he enunciates the words about writing makes the activity sound like macramé. "I can pay for you to visit your son in America four times a year; what do you think of that?"

"I want to make my own money," I repeat. "I like to work."

"Oh, my dear, you will have work, being my wife, taking care of the household, as grandmother to my future grandchildren, and mother to your son."

"That is not the kind of work I had in mind," I say.

He is quiet. After some moments of silence, I ask, "Would you like to be dependent on me financially?"

He shakes his head. "Not at all."

"So why is it so hard to understand I am uninterested in that?"

He has no answer.

We attend another Epiphany party at a chalet in the mountains. The hosts are former colleagues of the diplomat. A group of sixteen mingle in a large open room near a fire around a circular wooden table covered with delicious food. I overhear guests compliment me in the third person to each other and the diplomat. They call me *la americana*. The diplomat says, "She is also a *francesa.*"

Some ask, in different ways, what I am doing with the diplomat, which sets me to wonder further.

A chef pulls a suckling pig from the oven and places it in the center of the dining room table. The host offers me the first slices. She has been flirting with me since I arrived. Countless other delicious dishes pass from hand to hand around the long oval table. As I talk with a friend and former colleague of the diplomat about literature, and the theory that wounds are where all literature springs from, he looks up and across the table at the diplomat and says, "Did you hear that? This woman has just said something very interesting."

The diplomat looks away. I'm thinking how strange it is that he has said it to him instead of me.

The man sitting next to me leans closer to my ear and says, *"Lo peor es cuando ni te hacen caso, no?"* This can be translated as *the worst is when they don't even pay attention to you, isn't it?*

Another day, at a bookstore, I buy a book by a woman instead of the books by men the diplomat tells me I should buy. I ask if he knows the author. "I don't read women," he says.

"You're missing out," I say. "I like her column in the newspaper. I used her husband's account of Manhattan in a class. I am curious about hers."

The diplomat wants me to read his philosopher friend. I do and like him. Before we meet him for lunch, I say, "If he asks me questions, will you please let me answer them?"

He pulls his head back in astonishment. "Am I that much of a barbarian?"

"When people ask me questions, you often answer for me."

"I am very, very sorry," he says.

Yet, the majority of the time, he can't help himself.

We argue, and I want to go home. I board a train to Barcelona first.

Hours later, the newspapers I used to read lie on the red vinyl seat next to me, unread. The countryside we are rolling through, I have thoroughly read and am still reading, wanting to dissolve into it, to merge with the beauty.

Montserrat appears on the horizon, and I remember my annual pilgrimages there and climbing those mountains with people I love.

As the train approaches Barcelona Sants station, I ache to sit at Mom's feet; I ache for her hands on my shoulders and smoothing, playing with my hair as we watch dancing on television. This ache reminds me how she now sits in her apartment in the dark at night because she worries a man her daughter is divorcing will see her light on and stop. Bile, sadness, and guilt rise as I think how often I detour from seeing her because he might show up or be there. The train slows.

I walk through the station I know well. A friend, one of the advisors of my dissertation, is waiting for me in the parking lot in a new red Austin Mini. She drives us to one of my favorite neighborhoods in Barcelona, near Turo Park, and pulls up in front of a restaurant she loves, new to me. We sit at a table near a window, sunshine pooling onto the white table, flashing off the glasses and silverware. As we often used to, we eat delicious food, drink tasty wine, talk, laugh, and listen for hours–about life events, family, teaching, writing, scholarship, academia, colleagues, the UB, France, politics, and my friend's preparation to go to Berkeley as a visiting scholar.

"His kind is very macho," she says about the diplomat.

"He is asking me to dress more like the women in his city so that I stand out less."

She laughs as she says, "That's impossible."

We stroll around the pond and through Turo Park, and in the sunshine, outside on the terrace, we drink coffee at another old haunt of mine. It is January. 2016. I'm still married, despite my efforts to be single, and still receiving awful e-mails on that subject.

Back at Sants, I pause at the shop where I used to buy a small bag of candy for my son on the way home. I hesitate again at the top of the stairs I used to descend, then I follow the sign to another destination where I will meet the diplomat.

"You look terrible and exhausted," the housekeeper says when we return.

As soon as a local spa opens the following day, I am there. I swim in a Roman bath, linger with water jets, dawdle in tubs, then lie naked on a table surrounded by candles amid soft music. A kind, strong woman covers my body in warm clay, gently touches my shoulder, and says, "I will return in twenty minutes," then returns and massages me.

Afterward, another kind woman washes and styles my hair in a salon. On the way back to the diplomat's, I stop at the butcher shop for a specific sausage as I promised I would. When I open the apartment door, he is on his way out. The housekeeper smiles behind him. "I told you she would be prepared and on time."

It displeases him that I have taken care of myself, refusing his offer to pay for anything and that I am on time, and looking rejuvenated, sausage in hand, promise kept.

After lunch, the housekeeper mentions her desire to go to college and quit her job. The diplomat looks at me. "You might like the salary. It's not that much different than what you are making now."

This is the moment to end it. I sigh and think, I am leaving tomorrow anyway.

The housekeeper says something too quickly for me to understand, and the diplomat's tone suggests a playacted threat. The housekeeper rushes behind me like a child, saying, "Help me, help me; he says he is going to spank me."

"Spank?"

He raises his hand. I freeze. The housekeeper darts out of the room.

"You spank your housekeeper?" I ask.

"I could."

"Did you also spank your secretaries?"

"I could have. They would not have minded."

I back away in my chair. "That is violent," I say, then leave the table.

Upstairs, I look in the mirror and ask myself, "Who am I now? Where am I now? What am I doing now?" then I am silent for hours.

Later, the diplomat sits in the chair in the corner of the bedroom, near the closet where many of his dead wife's clothes still hang. "She would have reacted like you," he says.

What to do with that eludes me, but I take it as a compliment and confirmation. The thousands of miles of distance I am about to travel will give me the necessary time and space to decide what to do about his March visit to Dubuque and our visit together to California that I am already committed to.

Getting grief live from one man while getting it electronically from another has me dazed. I can only leave one man at a time. First things first, I tell myself.

My son hates to tell me he hit black ice on the way to pick me up at the airport. I am moved when I see how he duct-taped the bumper back onto the front of the car. We make it home. He drives his car back to Iowa City, and the insurance company provides me with a car while I wait on an estimate for the repair of mine. I begin a new semester of teaching.

All of my classes are in basement rooms without windows that last semester. It feels like I am teaching in bunkers.

TOTAL LOSS–in boldface type at the top of the car insurance papers– glares at me.

It is double-digits below zero.

My son is ill, and his university bill needs to be paid.

I am looking over the umpteenth version of the divorce stipulation.

"I sought you out, and you let me find you," the diplomat says over the phone after I remind him I had been wary of relationships with men when he approached me.

"Despite it all, I am thrilled to be back," I say to a friend.

"That says a lot," she answers.

"One student came to class five times out of twenty-five last fall and turned nothing in, then asked for a break at the end of the semester, and I made a deal with her. She met only a fraction of it and now is claiming it is unfair that she failed."

"Yep," a colleague says.

"Are you going to take this attitude lying down?" the visionary asks.

"I wish I could remain calm," I say.

"Steady might be a more attainable aim," she suggests.

"Your voice is necessary for women. You are part of a movement that is changing the world," the acupuncturist tells me.

At a friend's place, I draw a card from a deck on the table. Forgive someone, it says. I toss it back on the table.

"Not today? On vacation?" she asks.

And I laugh.

"I don't regret coming back here, and even though the teaching is less fulfilling than I hoped it would be, the life I have built around it is even richer than I imagined it could be," I tell another friend over dinner at my place.

"Stay strong. You have solid things around you," this friend who gives me gift certificates for massages says.

"A part of me just wants to scream," I say.

She looks out toward the piano room and upstairs. "This is a big house. You are alone in it. I say, let it rip. I mean after I go home."

Over the following days, I do, until I am hoarse and my throat hurts.

"You look like a lioness, Mom; you look good," my son tells me when he comes for a visit.

I replace the Cavalier with a Lancer, which seems a smart move.

I want to drive to national parks in the west. I want to move far and long and wide.

Four years later, I will, with a brand-new Insight.

In those last few days of January, sunshine again takes me by surprise, filling the sitting room and piano room and making the snow on the ground outside the windows all sparkly. It is my last January in Dubuque, but I don't know that yet.

S pring always comes.

"Let's be together now before making more plans," I say to the diplomat as I drive us away from O'Hare in March.

This bothers him.

"It feels strange not to feel like making love; maybe it is because I am tired," I say that night back home.

I put on my silk pajamas and get in bed next to him. He reaches for the buttons on my pajama top. "No," I say and push on his chest, but he is more forceful and bigger than me. It is over quickly, and he falls asleep immediately as I lie there, thinking about how I ask a guest, who has traveled far and given me much, to leave the day after he has arrived.

He is with me early the following morning as I am elected a state delegate representing the first woman to run for president on a major party ticket.

Back home in the kitchen, I say, "That was weird last night."

He shrugs as he says, "I needed a good night's sleep."

"I didn't sleep at all," I say.

He opens the refrigerator. While looking into it, he says, "It will never happen again."

It sounds strategic, more than repentant, and he is talking to the fruit.

It takes another day and a half to work up the courage to ask him to leave. I do it by saying I need to be alone. He takes it well for an hour or so. Then I think of my city grandma saying, "Why do people have to act so ugly?"

"That is not rape," a sister says three years later.

"The definition of rape is sexual penetration without consent. I said no."

"But he was in your bed."

"That doesn't mean it is open season for penetration," I say.

"Why didn't you immediately kick him out of your house and call the police?"

"For one reason, I wouldn't want to go through with them what I am going through with you right now." She is quiet, thinking deeply, and looks like Mom and Dad. "I wish I had kicked him out immediately," I say. "In a traumatic situation, I tend to freeze. I want to change that. I even spent time wondering about the kindest way to ask him to go."

"Woah. You are a kinder person than I."

"I don't know about that. I was exhausted. I had only been divorced a month and had my fill of dealing with the law and men. Can we stop talking about this?"

We are in her car, parked in front of a boutique in Pella. We've just come from the funeral of a college friend of hers. She looks at me. "It's just that I was shocked to hear you say that you had been raped, and I didn't know about it. I'm just saying that I am furious at that guy. I'd tell him what I think of him if he were in front of me. That's for sure."

"Thank you," I say.

S o, instead of going to California with the diplomat, I invite my son on a weekend road trip to Wyalusing State Park. We climb bluffs, collect wood and rock, and observe ferns and flowers. He hands me a walking stick, then offers to dig up a plant for me to take home. Pointing to a sign marked Immigrant Trail, he says, "Put up a wall," in the current president's accent.

He asks what happened as apologetic texts from the diplomat with requests to return make my phone sound like an alarm. "Let me put it this way: He couldn't take no for an answer," I say. "Still, I feel bad for him that I had to ask him to leave."

"Maybe you taught him something, Mom," my son says.

I love this kid.

In a shop on State Street in Madison, he holds up a t-shirt with a stick figure making a peace sign. "Mom, you have to get this; this is you."

I'm so happy he sees me this way.

During our lunch overlooking Lake Mendota, flashing in the sun, he sighs, then says, "This is the nicest town in the Midwest."

I nod. It's lovely to be at peace, in the sunshine, on a beautiful lake, with my child at my side.

"See your grandfather standing there. Tell him he handicapped you from being yourself, and that was a high price to pay for the strength you took away from that experience," the visionary says, and I do.

Then I do a version of this with the diplomat.

"Now, see your son's father. Tell him how much and deeply you were hurt and how you hurt each other."

I do.

"Now, thank him if it feels true."

I stroke my throat as if that might help the words come. "It feels false," I say.

"It is important to know there is still a tie there, then, if you cannot thank him."

Later, and elsewhere, I am happy to read that this is a belief rather than fact and, thankfully, unnecessary.

During some dark days alone, I rest and ask myself questions like, did I ignore my hurt? Yes.

I ask myself how often people said, "That would be so painful," before I realized, yes, ouch. I feel again the value of admitting hurt, of recognizing victimhood, however temporary that position may be. It rains, and the grass becomes greener. I stay inside and upstairs, often standing and looking out the back window. I feel afraid even to go to the grocery store. I fear turning on the lights and being seen from the outside. It is strange to feel scared of my own family. Irrationally petrified, I ask myself, "What's that about?"

"How scary that was," is the answer that tumbles out of my mouth.

I feel like the girl I was when Grandpa touched me into confusion and out of trust.

"I feel so alone, and yet I know there are people out there who love me, but it is as if I am frozen inside, petrified to go to the grocery store, and I need food. Seeing people sounds awful," I tell the visionary when she calls hours later. She has a way of calling when I am bereft and silent.

"You're raw, growing a new skin. I wish you had called me. Breathe. You're holding your breath. Now, sit in a chair and feel your feet on the ground. Close your eyes." She guides me through a weeping howl, frozen since I held it back to save my family from pain. "Now, open our eyes. Keep your feet on the ground. Look around. You are safe. You are grown up. He is gone. You can go outside. You are safe."

That word, *safe*, opens a view of myself at 14 and the moment I deemed life precarious. I see how this realization of precarity inspired my strategy to build the courage to live a life I love.

Over the following hours, I trace the feeling of danger with my grandfather next door while I was an adolescent to my son's father's proximity and strange behavior on the sidewalk and the way I feel again a painful need to run away from a beloved home to protect myself.

I see how far from myself I went to reach the place the man I loved dwells, how my values were explored and tested in that journey, expanding me, and showing me my limits. I see how fighting for respect while staying meant I accepted the lack and the fighting, trapping myself in the hope for change.

This hope is a misplaced loyalty to a relationship instead of to self, to life. I wish these realizations had dawned on me earlier. This knowledge I can be thankful for, I say as I pace the house, up and down stairs until finally, I sleep.

I return to the university to teach.

It is good to see Mom and my sisters in a café that night. To sing happy birthday to one and share some cake. And then to give Mom a ride home and watch ice skating on television with her.

In the Colorado Desert, in the spring of 2020, I start to say I still feel hurt and angry, and then I pause and look at myself in the mirror and ask, "Is that true? Do I?"

Something has shifted, and the pain is less accessible.

"Where does the hurt go?" I wonder.

"Who cares?" I answer, then dance.

That last April in Dubuque, a few weeks after spring break, a producer introduces himself to me at a local film festival. Throughout one weekend, we enjoy lively conversations about writers, writing, and films, and we dance, eat, watch movies, and visit the area. He recites poetry to me with the river as a backdrop.

A few weeks later, he sends me first-class tickets to the Pacific Northwest, and we continue our conversation. He's a great conversationalist. It seems a bit early when he asks to take my hand, but I let him. In the end, I'll know sticking with conversation would have been the best choice. At that point, I still feel like I have to push myself to move on. Yet, I'm determined to go slowly this time. I have my own hotel room, and though he does get frustrated with me for staying with the holding-hands phase, we have a good time. I especially love the seaplane ride over Puget Sound he offers after I mention it looks fun.

"Where do you find these guys?" a friend asks.

"They just turn up," I say.

The men I meet after I leave my marriage appear in front of me, offering me pleasure. With each, I feel some sort of attraction, unable to define immediately, along with blurry concern, which eventually coagulates into disappointment. The fuzzy problem, I learn, is my misty connection to my trustworthy intuition.

In Dubuque, as spring turns toward summer, I wake at dawn and swim at seven, then once home, I pick raspberries, eat breakfast, job search, translate, and garden, staying in my bathing suit to keep life feeling as much like a vacation as possible.

I often take Mom for drives and doctor appointments in the afternoons and run errands. I occasionally meet friends in the evenings.

I think about everybody leaving the party of life as I watch my parents' generation dwindle.

The producer calls and texts often. He invites me for a weekend in Chicago. I love swimming on a hotel's rooftop and our conversations over breakfast. I love kissing.

Then he comes to Iowa, and while I drive him to Spillville and back, he drops hints that he thinks I am rich financially and says and does other strange things that make me feel he misunderstands me and is hiding something. I see his disappointment when he finds out I am unemployed. He's already on his phone trying to find me a job when he needs one. He admits this much.

"Where is your former husband?" he asks as I drive into town.

"There," I say and point to the man on the bicycle in front of us.

When I drop the producer at the airport, he asks if he can come back. "Nah," I say, in so many words.

I find it hard to put words to my feelings. This opening and closing of relationships, the way I feel hints of awkwardness yet am still willing to explore what seems like richness, and how I can be fooled by people performing acts of kindness. It surprises me how people can get me wrong when they sum me up, even though I am not pretending.

That night, unable to sleep, I plant flowers in the dark, then sit for a long time in the sanctuary. Then I go to the kitchen and eat a slice of melon from a friend's farm.

When I come home from a walk in mid-June, my son is resting on the glider on the porch. I fire up the grill, and we sit on the back patio amid flaming torches and the song of cicadas, enjoying pork chops with rosemary, figs, walnuts, green beans, corn, and home-grown tomatoes with home-made pesto.

"I gotta tell you, Mom, I love your backyard. It reminds me of Castillon."

Your sounds strange, but I let it go and chuckle. "I've turned this patch of Iowa into the south of France?"

"You have." He points to the little red flowers that look like lipsticks. "Those plants are brilliant. I've seen fast-motion videos on climbing plants like yours on the internet." He sighs, "I'm sad you have to leave this house, Mom."

"That's unsure yet," I say as I glance at the about-to-open purple bell flowers near the flourishing geraniums, then lift a freshly picked raspberry from a glass bowl and pop it in my mouth.

I love being with him and watching him grow up. I love that he loves the garden and coming home to this house after all that's happened. He is spending his summer in Iowa City, working, and enjoying friends. His first year at university has gone well. The dissolution is final. We are moving on.

For now, I enjoy the precious moment.

"I just wish Daddy would have lived longer," Mom says. We are lying on her bed.

"Me, too, Mom. Yesterday I dreamed he died again, and this time I was there."

Sometimes she says, "I just want to die."

"I would help you, Mom, if I could, but then I'd have to spend the rest of my life in jail, and we'd both hate that."

"We sure would, honey. I'll stop talking nonsense."

As I lie there, I wonder when I'd like to die. Maybe the same time of year as now, when Dad died, the first days of summer, after one final gorgeous spring.

Remembering the soothing breeze as we walked out of the church in the funeral procession, I imagine it is probably the easiest time of year for those left behind. It is difficult to imagine my son on earth without me. I wonder if this will get easier as we both get older. I remember Mom saying, "It's hard for me to watch you kids getting older," and wondering what she meant. She couldn't explain when I asked. I imagine it is about the marching of time, the knowledge that one day we will all be gone, all our beloveds, poof. Immortals, I tell myself, we're immortals. We'll find a way, and until then, let's enjoy our time.

Mom and I love the cool night breezes through the open windows on our bare legs and arms. When her breathing sounds regular, and I can tell her rest is real, I roll quietly to the edge of the bed and stand.

She wakes and insists on following me to the door. I hug her and look into her eyes as I say, "You look so good, Mom, you do." Because she does. The rest, love, being listened to and massaged–all show on her face.

She makes flirty fluttering eyes. "Well, if I look so good," she says, "let me change back out of my nightgown, and we'll go out."

How hard it is to leave, and how hard it can be to stay.

"I'm so tired of sitting around and thinking about everything," Mom says one morning when I call.

"So that's where I get it from," I say.

"I'd just like to see the kids."

I drive her to her granddaughter's. "And that's where Daddy is," she says as we pass the cemetery.

Later, after seeing my niece and her kids, when I turn onto Highway 1 to take her to see her grandson in Iowa City, she says, "Daddy and I were on this highway many times."

After lunch with my son, and on the way home, she asks, "So where is his father?"

"I think he is still in town. People keep asking me why he is staying. I tell them to ask him."

"Maybe he is staying for me," she says, then winks.

Then she looks out into the cornfields and says, "I just worry about you girls."

"Your three kind, intelligent, accomplished daughters?" I ask.

"They are just like their mother, aren't they?" she says.

We stop for a root beer near home. Mom's blue eyes fire when I tell her at least half of her children are fans of the offender running for president. "That's ridiculous. What the hell is the matter with them?" she asks.

I shrug. Lightning bolts in the north, so I drive us in that direction, along the river, and up the bluffs, watching storm clouds roll in. The wind whips branches, littering the road. "Doesn't it look like the end of the world, Mom?"

"I've never wanted to see the end of the world. This is spooky. Let's get out of here. Your dad is watching right now, wondering what the hell we are doing."

I think Dad would enjoy it, but the odds of knowing him are in her favor. I drive her home, and in the elevator, she says, "Nobody knows what it's like."

I caress her back. "I imagine many other folks here might know what it's like. Though for sure, no one knows what it is like to be you."

I leave when she is feeling better.

One August afternoon, the silence and aloneness in the house bend me in half. I reach for the kitchen table to brace myself, grab a pen, and write; *I believe there are riches in this solitude if I can stand the unknowing.*

Then, I take my sunglasses in for repair. When the young male technician hands them back to me, he says, "There will be no charge for the screw."

I chuckle.

He blushes.

That night I step into the poet's going-away party in the house where I lived when I arrived. Her mother takes one look at me, sways her hips, and says, "Whenever I see you, I think of dancing."

om's television blasts down the hallway. I give up on knocking and call her from my cellphone. "Mom, open the door. I am here."

When she does, her face brightens, and she spreads her arms wide for a hug, which we both enjoy.

I pick up the telephone receiver on the table to hang it back on the wall, and she grabs my arm. "Wait. Stop. She might still be on the line," she says.

"She is me, Mom," I say.

"Well, where the hell have you been?" she asks.

I've stayed at home for some days, quiet. "Taking care of myself," I answer.

She squishes up her face as if this is a new scent or taste, and she would be unopposed to trying it.

As she falls asleep, I ask, "Mom, was I your favorite?"

"Yes," she says, then pauses. "What else did you think I was going to say?"

I love these playful moments.

I am at Mom's side for the last sixteen days of her life. Bright sunshine and shadows of tree branches on the snow are visible through the windows. She becomes more peaceful and youthful as she leaves. Her six children gather around her, and we pray, talk, laugh, and tease. She is conscious and kissing and asking for more kisses; her voice is soft and tired, so sometimes she purses her lips and lifts her chin towards each of us instead of speaking. This is the death she hoped for.

In her last moments, my sisters and I are stretched horizontally at the side of her bed, preparing to sleep. It's almost midnight. This closeness reminds me of summer nights at the cottage when my elder sister and I shared a bed, and our baby sister slept in the crib next to us. "Mom," I hear my elder sister say, then she encircles my ankle with her hand. "I think she's gone," she whispers.

We three daughters sit up, side by side, lean over Mom, and watch as a nurse checks her pulse, then nods to confirm her departure. Only moments before, we were outside the room joking and imagining the possible newspaper headlines like Three Dead Daughters Carried Out of Nursing Home Before Ninety-One-Year-Old Mother.

"What do we do now?" we say simultaneously.

I wish we had sat with her body for a while to feel for her spirit in the room, talked, and sang to her soul. Yet, we did that a lot before she left. It's awful to know she's dead and impossible to wish her back to the suffering ordeal we all feel relief from amid the grief.

Elder sister calls the brothers. Eldest brother will call his friend, the undertaker. Two sisters leave the room to call their significant others, and I deflate the air bed to do something. I look at Mom lying there, so still in her blue nightgown. Each day of those last sixteen, I washed and moisturized her face, then powdered it and swept her cheekbones with a blush before styling her hair the way she liked it. I talked and whispered to her, wanted her always to feel someone near, so sometimes I slept on the floor beside her with my arm up on her bed, holding her hand. This was as much for me as for her. As I lay there at night, the full moon shining on me, I loved listening to her breathing; it was like being in the womb outside of the body.

All that touching, all those days, a lifetime of touching, and now I stay back as if frozen. Her body is like a sacred, untouchable relic. It's weird. It doesn't even occur to me that she might still be there. She left us so slowly, then the instant she could.

I stand there stiffly, watching her like a Queen's Guard until the brothers walk in. They sit down and gaze at her body, with pain morphing on their faces. It feels like a changing of the guard. I know the undertakers will arrive soon, zip Mom's body into a bag, then carry her out, and I will spare myself the sight of that.

I sleep at a sister's in a bed Mom often slept in. She comes to me in my dreams that night, lifts a veil from my heart, then twirls with it. Dad joins her, and they dance and laugh.

Months later, she will come again, in a vision, and hand me the full moon on a platter.

"If this is what you want—the house and writing and traveling—then do it," I repeat to myself that last July in Dubuque.

What can only I write? I ask myself.

Myself, I answer.

Should I start with everything that's happened since the first novel? I ask.

That would be enough to lay me out, is the answer.

I rearrange the back patio furniture so I can see flowers from each writing position.

I notice that someone—a squirrel, rabbit, chipmunk, or deer—ate the red coneflower buds. And I feel sad about all the work the seed did only to be denied a bloom.

Under the parasol, amid light rain and thunder, I begin.

I am aware I am living a dream.

All that is missing is a freshwater pool.

I sense I need to be alone to write what I have to write.

Sometimes, in the beginning, in Dubuque, I write in the sanctuary and smile each time I look up at the painting of flying turtles.

On Sunday mornings, I hear singing from the church while I tend the flowers.

I especially enjoy "Hallelujah!"

"Today I was looking at job openings in St. Louis, St. Paul, Grinnell," I tell Mom one late summer evening.

"Don't leave," she says. "Not until I die."

"Do you have a date on that, Mom?"

"I'll have to get that settled," she says.

Three days before Mom dies, my sisters, niece, and I dance around her bed to the big band music she loves.

She sits up and dances with us to "In the Mood."

I glance at the stack of freshly released *Lucy, go see.* hardcovers on her nightstand, and I am in the back seat of the Country Squire again, Mom driving me to the bookmobile on a country road.

That afternoon, after a long drive through the rolling snowy hills and valleys, I walk back into her room, and she's propped up in a sitting position, so I sit down on the bed facing her. I kiss her, then look into her eyes and say, "I was singing along with old love songs on KDTH as I drove north on 52, Mom, and you know what I realized? I was singing them all to you."

She nuzzles the tip of her nose with mine.

"You are the best love story of my life," I say.

She bats her eyes.

I kiss her cheek and whisper, "Thank you for bringing me home, Mom."

That makes her happy, I can tell.

My aunt tells me about bittersweet at lunch this past summer, 2022, and how her mom and dad loved it. How they'd call her and say, "Are you sure you have enough bittersweet? Come and get some, or we'll bring it to you. It's good to have."

It grows rampant.

She tells me how Grandpa used to bring more of it every time he came.

"And now it's all over the place, bittersweet everywhere," she says, opening her arms.

I close this book surprised by the uncanny parallel between Lucy Pilgrim's path and mine. She flies toward Barcelona on the last page of *Lucy, go see.* As I write on this page, I am preparing to return to that marvelous city.

"I knew it was only a matter of time before you came home," a dear friend said when I called.